INDO-PACIFIC
CORAL REEF
FIELD GUIDE

Dr. Gerald R. Allen & Roger Steene

ISBN : 981-00-5687-7

Editions in : 1994 • 1995 • 1996 • 1998 • 1999

Publisher :
TROPICAL REEF RESEARCH
362 Upper Paya Lebar Road, #04-06 Da Jin Factory Bldg., Singapore 534963. Tel: (65) 487 6966 • Fax: (65) 487 6466
Email: brand@cyberway.com.sg

Typeset and printed by :
Calendar Print Pte. Ltd., Singapore.

Colour seperation by :
Colourscan Pte Ltd, Singapore.

Australia Representative :
Coral Sea Imagery
P. O. Box 2186, Townsville, QLD 4810, Australia
Tel: (61) 7-4721-1633 • Fax: (61) 7-4721-1477
Email: info@coral-sea.com.au

North America Representative:
Odyssey Publishing
11558 Rolling Hills Drive, El Cajon, California, U.S.A.
Tel: (1) 619-579-8405 • Fax : (1) 619 -579 7901
Email: odyssey@adnc.com

Acknowledgements

We are very grateful for the assistance received from the following invertebrate specialists who gave freely of their valuable time in order to identify our photographs: Mr. Phil Alderslade, Northern Territory Museum, Australia (alcyonarians); Dr. Avril Ayling, Daintree, Queensland (sponges); Dr. Gerald Bakus, University of Southern California (sponges); Dr. Rick Braley, Townsville, Australia (giant clams); Dr. A. J. Bruce, Northern Territory Museum (shrimps); Mr. Clay Bryce, Western Australian Museum (molluscs); Dr. Eric Coppejans, Laboratorium voor Morfologie, Systematien en Ecologie van de Planten, Gent, Belgium (green algae); Dr. Peter Davie, Queensland Museum (crustaceans); Dr. Daphne Fautin, University of Kansas (anemones); Dr. Jane Fromont, Townsville, Queensland (sponges); Dr. Terry Gosliner, California Academy of Sciences (nudibranchs); Dr. Russell Hanley, Northern Territory Museum, (worms); Dr. Peter Hayward, University College of Swansea (bryozoans); Dr. John Hooper, Queensland Museum (sponges); Dr. Pat Hutchins, Australian Museum (worms); Dr. Matthew Jebb, Christensen Research Institute, Madang, Papua New Guinea (algae); Mrs. Diane Jones, Western Australian Museum (crustaceans); Mrs. Loisette Marsh, Western Australian Museum (echinoderms); Dr. Pat Mather, Queensland Museum (ascidians); Dr. Leslie Newman, Queensland Museum (flat-worms); Dr. Mark Norman, Museum of Victoria, Australia (cephalopods); Dr. W. F. Prud'homme van Reine, Rijksherbarium, Leiden, The Netherlands (brown and red algae); Dr. Clyde Roper, Smithsonian Institution (cephalopods); Dr. John Ryland, University College of Swansea (bryozoans);

Mrs. Shirley Slack-Smith, Western Australian Museum (algae); Mr. Laurie Smith, Western Australian Museum (sea snakes); Dr. Lyle Vail, Lizard Island Marine Research Laboratory, Queensland (crinoids); Dr. Charlie Veron, Australian Institute of Marine Sciences (hard corals); Dr. Jan Watson, Melbourne, Victoria (hydrozoans); Dr. Fred Wells, Western Australian Museum (molluscs); and Dr. Gary Williams, California Academy of Sciences (soft corals).

We also thank Mr. Clay Bryce, Dr. Peter Kuhn, Dr. Leslie Newman, Dr. Jack Randall, Mr. Nick Tonks, and Dr. Lyle Vail for allowing us to use their photographs.

A significant portion of the field work for this volume was conducted at the excellent facilities of the Christensen Research Institute at Madang, Papua New Guinea. We are espe-cially grateful to the Director of the Institute, Dr. Matthew Jebb and his wife Serina, for their enthusiastic support of our project.

Our diving activities were greatly assisted by Mr. Mark Allen, Mr. Brian Bailey, Mr. Rudie Kuiter, Dr. Tim Meagher, Mr. Wally Siagian, Dr. Walter Starck, Mr. Jim Tobin, and staff of the Cairns Underwater Camera Centre (Queensland, Australia).

Connie Allen assisted with typing duties and prepared the index. Finally, we wish to acknowledge the considerable time and effort contributed by Bernard Koh of Calendar Print, Singapore in producing this volume.

This book is dedicated to the memory of Josephine Steene.

C O N T E N T S

Coral Reefs
Nature's Richest Realm

Coral reefs are certainly one of our planet's greatest natural attractions. Due to their abundance of species and great ecological complexity they are frequently compared to tropical rainforests. But, in terms of sheer abundance of readily observable animal life, even the mighty rainforest takes a back seat. In the rainforest one must be either lucky or a trained observer to watch many of the animal inhabitants involved in their daily activities. But even a first-time snorkeler will be absolutely overwhelmed by the parade of exotic life forms on a coral reef.

What are the forces in nature that have shaped the coral reef environment? Both coral reefs and rainforests derive their primary energy from solar radiation, and therefore thrive in areas of maximum sunlight. For this reason coral reef development is optimum where sea temperatures are warmest, generally between the latitudes of 30 degrees north and south. These coordinates roughly coincide with the 20 degree Centigrade isotherms, which is considered the minimum temperature for sustained coral reef development. Isolated coral colonies and individual growths may occur in cooler waters, but very few massive coral structures are found in subtropical seas. Two notable exceptions are Lord Howe Island and the Abrolhos Islands, on the respective eastern and western coasts of Australia. These reefs owe their existence to warm southward flowing currents.

Optimum coral reef development is also strongly correlated with clean, clear water, and relatively shallow depths. The energy supply of a coral reef originates from plants, which only thrive in shallow, sun drenched areas. Productivity is decreased or eliminated in areas subjected to dirty, sediment-laden water, as is the case around the mouth of large rivers. The correlation of coral growth and clear water is readily evident along most tropical shorelines. For example, reef development along the Queensland coast of Australia is very poor in comparison to the luxuriant offshore areas of the Great Barrier Reef. The same pattern is evident, albeit on a much smaller scale, around a tropical islet. Coral growth is usually sparse immediately adjacent to the shore, but often increases dramatically as one swims seaward.

Fossil evidence indicates that coral reefs are an extremely ancient phenomena. They first appeared more than 400 million years ago. These early corals have long been extinct. It was not until the past 25 million years, rather recent on the geological time scale, that modern forms evolved. Coral reefs, as seen today, represent a developmental episode of only about 5,000 years or less. During this period sea levels have remained relatively stable. Approximately 15,000 years ago seas were as much as 120 meters below the present level. Coral reef development is closely tied to these fluctuating sea levels as will be explained below.

◄ Coral reefs are truly nature's richest realm.

Introduction

Building Blocks

Individual coral animals, most of which exist in colonies, are the primary building blocks of the reef. They depend on microscopic unicellular plants (zooxanthellae) that live within their tissue to provide the bulk of their nutrition. This plant "fuel" facilitates growth and secretion of the all-important calcium carbonate skeleton that provides the reef's structural framework. The beautiful living corals that adorn the reef are actually a very small part of the overall reef structure. They form a thin veneer that overlies a solid limestone (calcium carbonate) foundation. This platform is composed of skeletal remains of past coral generations as well as numerous reef-dwelling animals that have hard parts or shells composed of calcium carbonate. The most obvious contributors are various molluscs, crustaceans, and echinoderms, but forams (single-celled organisms), sponges, soft corals, worms, and fishes also add to the skeletal matrix. Certain plants, most notably green algae of the genus *Halimeda*, secrete calcium carbonate and in some areas it contributes greatly to bottom sediments.

Therefore, a great variety of animals and plants provide the raw ingredients or basic building blocks for the reef's foundation. These materials are bound together into a consolidated structure by an important group of plants, known as calcareous or coralline red algae. These algae do not resemble plants in the traditional sense, lacking leaves, stems, and roots. Instead they form a pink or red colored crust of limestone that virtually cements the reef's framework. Coralline algae are readily visible to divers, snorkelers, and reef walkers, particularly on the upper, wave exposed edge of outer reef slopes.

Maldive Islands, an atoll paradise in the Indian Ocean.

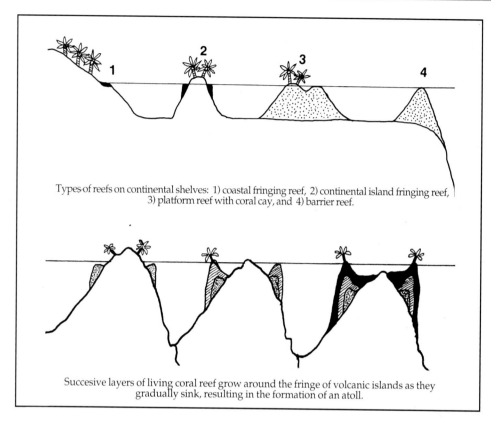

Types of reefs on continental shelves: 1) coastal fringing reef, 2) continental island fringing reef, 3) platform reef with coral cay, and 4) barrier reef.

Succesive layers of living coral reef grow around the fringe of volcanic islands as they gradually sink, resulting in the formation of an atoll.

Darwin's Theory

Charles Darwin was the first to formulate a theory that is now widely accepted concerning the origin and structure of coral reefs. This theory is based on the concept that given the proper conditions of clean, warm water, coral will proliferate in shallow seas. Darwin concluded that an oceanic atoll was originally formed as a fringing reef that encircled the shallow margin of a volcanic island. As the island gradually sinks (a few millimeters annually) the living corals grow upward in successive layers to maintain contact with optimum light conditions. An atoll therefore marks the final stages of sinking. The former island has disappeared beneath the waves, but the fringing reef persists as a ring around a central lagoon. Darwin's theory has since been tested by experimental drilling at several sites. For example, at Enewetak Atoll in the central Pacific a volcanic base was discovered at a depth of 1,219 meters.

Various types of reef structures are shown in the accompanying illustration. Continental land masses and offshore islands may possess a variety of associated coral structures, including fringing reefs, platform (or mid-lagoon) reefs, and an outer barrier reef. Barrier reefs originate from fringing reefs, in a process that is similar to atoll formation. These reefs are gradually separated from the mainland due to subsidence of the land mass. Conversely, rising sea levels could achieve the same result.

Limestone islets and fringing coral reefs abound in the Andaman Sea off western Thailand.

Reef reflections such as this occur only on exceptionally calm days.

Superabundance of life

Why do coral reefs support such a super-abundance of life? This question is even more perplexing in view of the fact that clear, tropical oceans are notoriously low in nutrients. This problem is overcome by the independent nature of coral reef systems. The reef's plants, particularly the tiny zooxanthellae, are the real secret of it's success. They utilize sunlight and carbon dioxide to produce energy-rich organic compounds. The plants are the food source of a host of invertebrates and fishes, thus forming the vital first step in the coral reef food chain, often referred to as a feeding web due to the tangled inter-relationships of consumer and consumed organisms.

Coral reefs are indeed nature's richest realm. They are extremely complex systems, consisting of numerous microhabitats. The huge number of species found on coral reefs is a direct reflection of the high number of habitat opportunities afforded by this environment. In addition to the obvious community of plants and animals seen on or above the reef's surface, there are thousands of unseen organisms. Diverse communities live under rocks and dead coral slabs, or in the crevices and fissures of the reef. An incredible number of species are associated with live and dead coral heads. A single head may contain more than 100 species of worms and a numerous assortment of other organisms!

Symbiotic associations are also extremely common. For example, sponges, soft and hard corals, echinoderms, and ascidians frequently have crustaceans, molluscs, worms, and fishes living on their outer surface or within internal cavities. In addition, a community of macroscopic and microscopic animals live below the surface of sand and rubble bottoms. Finally, there is a legion of microscopic creatures that live either on the reef's surface or in mid-water directly above. The latter are referred to as zooplankton, a mixture of larval and adult forms, that are an important food source for many reef inhabitants.

It is difficult to avoid being totally overwhelmed by the abundance and variety of life on a coral reef. This is especially true for first-time visitors. Is it possible to make any sense of this seemingly unordered chaos? Don't despair. All that's necessary is a rudimentary knowledge of the way in which plants and animals are classified and a few simple facts about their biology. Given this background, even novices can reap the same sort of satisfaction from their reef experience that is usually reserved for seasoned divers or marine scientists.

Basic needs

In order to appreciate and understand the coral reef's abundant diversity of life forms keep in mind a few simple concepts. First, all plants and animals must fulfill several basic needs in order to survive : 1) they must obtain nutrients from the surrounding environment to sustain energy levels; 2) they must exchange oxygen and carbon dioxide (respiration); 3) they must avoid predation; and 4) they must reproduce to ensure the survival of future generations. Second, every species that you see on the reef has a distinct life style that allows it to fulfill these basic needs in its own unique way. And third, the external appearance of plants and animals reveals a great deal about how they are specially adapted to survive in their environment.

Every animal on the reef, be it a fish, worm, or sea urchin, is a unique success story with regards to its ability to survive in a complex environment. The streamlined shape of a fish,

The Seychelles are a popular coral reef destination for European vacationers.

along with its muscular development, presence of fins, and forward position of the eyes and mouth succinctly conveys that it is a highly mobile hunter or grazer. By contrast, the non-streamlined, radial symmetry of sea urchins and starfish definitely indicate a slow-moving creature. A closer look reveals that their lack of mobility is compensated by defensive armament in the form of spines and bony plates. Feeding options are definitely more limited than for fishes. Therefore it is not surprising that the diet includes items such as sea weeds, organic detritus, and attached or slow-moving invertebrates such as oysters, clams, and coral.

Environmental conditions exert a great influence in determining how an individual organism copes with its basic needs. Over long periods of time, thousands or even millions of years, succeeding generations of a particular species become gradually modified in a manner that allows them to most efficiently utilize their environment. The end result is an organism that is finely tuned to its surroundings. This phenomenon is clearly evident when comparing soft and hard corals of shallow, exposed reef flats with those of deeper waters. Species in exposed shallows tend to be much more robust, and therefore resistant to wave damage. Those living on deeper parts of the reef frequently exhibit a more delicate structure, and may grow to a very large size. This is why huge formations of table-top *Acropora* coral and massive gorgonian sea fans are never seen in wave-exposed areas.

Always be first and foremost an observer in the underwater realm. But in order to receive maximum benefit from your reef encounter

Crystal waters, excellent reefs, and beautiful island scenery are prime attractions on the Indonesian island of Flores.

proceed that extra step. Remember to pay close attention to details of external anatomy, behavior, and habitat. These will provide substantial clues in unlocking the coral reefs many secrets.

What's in a name?

Although the fundamentals of biological nomenclature and classification are common knowledge for many, the average person frequently has little idea of the basis of scientific names or how plants and animals are classified. There's no need to panic at the sight of the unpronounceable scientific names that appear in the photographic captions of this book. They are part of a clever classification system introduced by the Swedish botanist, Carole Linnaeus, in the mid-18th Century. In order to facilitate the exchange of knowledge

between scientists regardless of their native tongue, Linnaeus devised a universal standard for naming biological organisms. At the heart of this system is the binomial or double word that pertains to the genus and species. Every described organism, be it a weed, single-celled amoeba, crab, fish, or human being, has a two-part scientific name that is most often formed from Latin or Greek words. The first part is the genus or generic name and the second is the species or specific name (**these names are generally italicized**).

Of course it is more practical to use common names of plants and animals. No one can deny that Regal Angelfish rolls off the tongue much easier than *Pygoplites diacanthus*. There is now a well established list of common names for fishes, birds, amphibians, reptiles, and mammals. But names other than scientific

A coral cay in the Sulu Sea between Borneo and the Philippines.

ones are totally lacking for numerous invertebrate species as can be seen when browsing through the pages of this book. Pronouncing the scientific names is not all that difficult if one slowly enunciates each syllable. There is no need to feel self conscious about mispronouncing these names. There is seldom agreement on their pronunciation, even among scientists!

When translated with the aid of a Latin dictionary the genus and species names are often descriptive. For example such names as *micrognathus* (small jaw), *rubripinnis* (red fin), *longirostris* (long nose), and *albimaculatus* (white-spotted) may allude to a dominant characteristic of the organism. Species are also named after people (these end with -i

or ae; eg. *smithi* or *elizabethae*) or places (often ending in -ensis; eg. *hawaiiensis* or *japanensis*).

In order to be officially recognized the scientific name of a plant or animal must appear in a scientific publication and be accompanied by sufficient descriptive information to distinguish it from close relatives. Hundreds of new species are described every year. Although the majority of the Earth's vertebrates have been scientifically cataloged, there are still thousands of invertebrates that lack scientific names. Quite simply, there are not enough scientists, particularly for the study of groups that have huge numbers, insects being a prime example.

Exploring Australia's Great Barrier Reef. ➤

C l a s s i f i c a t i o n

The study of biological classification is generally known as taxonomy and scientists who specialize in plant or animal classification are called taxonomists. In this modern age of specialization individual researchers tend to concentrate on a particular group, for example hard corals, or may even specialize further, focusing on a single family of corals or group of related families. The aim of every taxonomist, regardless of their speciality, is to formulate a classification scheme that reflects the true relationships that exist in nature.

The species is the fundamental unit of biological classification. Different types of plants and animals are placed into natural groups, often, but not always, indicated by their structural similarities.

For example, tigers and domestic cats are clearly separate species, but have many similar external and internal features. Although each is sufficiently distinct to be classified in a different genus, their overall similarity indicates a common line of ancestry. They are therefore placed in the same family, Felidae **(family names can be recognized by their spelling, which generally ends in -idae)**. In similar fashion, related families are placed in the same Order. Again using the cat family as an example, it is placed in the same Order (Carnivora), as dogs and foxes (both in the family Canidae). The highest rungs on the "ladder" of classification pertain to Class and Phylum. Most of the chapters in this book are devoted to these two highest categories.

The classification of the Emperor angelfish is presented as an example :

> **PHYLUM :** Chordata (all animals with a notochord)
> **CLASS :** Osteichthyes (all bony fishes)
> **ORDER :** Perciformes (most reef fish families)
> **FAMILY :** Pomacanthidae (marine angelfishes)
> **GENUS :** *Pomacanthus* (closely related angelfishes)
> **SPECIES :** *imperator* (the Emperor angelfish)

Juvenile Emperor angelfish,
Pomacanthus imperator
(adult illustrated on
page 305).

The Evolutionary Tree

This diagram gives a very simplified overview of the higher classification of plants and animals presented in this book. In general, there is an increase in complexity of structural organization for each group proceeding towards the top of the tree.

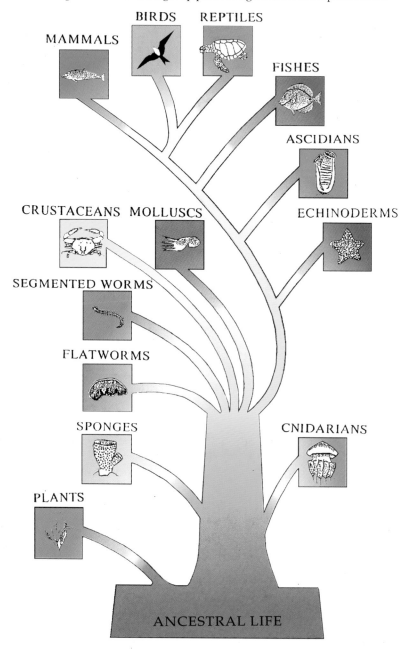

Introduction

Conservation

There is growing concern about the rapid decline of coral reefs in many parts of the globe. Fishing with explosives has caused wholesale destruction of reefs, particularly in Malaysia, Indonesia, and the Philippines. We did not appreciate the severity of this problem until a recent trip to northern Borneo. Underwater explosions were heard (and felt!) on nearly every dive, sometimes as many as three or four on a single dive! We also witnessed numerous "bald spots" where coral had been destroyed by previous blasting. Clearly it is up to local governments to eliminate these destructive practices, but this is easier said than done.

Australian authorities have registered concern about the increased use of many areas within the Great Barrier Reef Marine Park. An unprecedented tourist boom has resulted in one million visitors to the Reef each year. In addition, an affluent Australian society means that power boats are plentiful and the average citizen has more leisure time. Consequently there is heavy visitation of many reef areas, particularly those within 1-2 hours cruising time of the mainland. One of the main issues is coral damage due to random anchoring, snorkeling activities, and reef walking, and also uncontrolled fishing, especially spear-fishing. As a result protective zoning has now been implemented over much of the reef.

It is up to every reef visitor to practice their own personal code of conservation. It is plain common sense to avoid coral damage, or to catch just enough fish for a meal instead of 20 or 30. It is certainly OK to touch reef animals and plants. This is part and parcel of the reef experience, but avoid causing damage. The basic rule is to leave things as you find them.

This means returning dead coral slabs and rocks to their original position after examining the fascinating wealth of invertebrate life on their bottom surface.

Although many conservationists would have you believe that the world's coral reefs are disappearing at a rapid rate, all is not doom and gloom. Reefs are incredibly resistant to all sorts of destructive forces, both man-made and natural. Coral that is destroyed for one reason or another is not gone forever. Recolonization by reef organisms begins almost immediately and coral communities can be restored within a period of 15-20 years. Harmful as it is, the sort of damage caused by reef walkers and anchors pales to insignificance when compared to the lethal natural forces that continually threaten reefs. Familiar natural disasters such as cyclones, tidal waves, and earthquakes are equally devastating underwater as they are on land. Reef systems are also self-destructive through the action of myriad coral-feeding and boring organisms. In actual fact these destructive agents are vital for the continued existence of coral reefs. As mentioned in a previous section, the calcium carbonate "debris" of reef organisms is eventually "cemented", forming a solid platform for future coral growth.

Starfish plagues and bleaching

Over the past few decades alarm bells have been raised over the plague-like infestation of the coral-eating Crown-of-thorns starfish (*Acanthaster*). A number of theories have been offered to account for this population explosion, including man-made pollution. However, there is now evidence that periodic infestations are a natural cycle that has been occurring for centuries. Of more recent concern is a phenomenon known as "coral bleaching". This is caused by the loss of nutrient-giving symbiotic algae that live within the coral tissue and are largely responsible for its color. As a result, isolated heads or entire coral thickets become ghostly white. Some corals may mysteriously recover, but if the problem persists for more than a few weeks they eventually starve to death. A total of 60 major bleaching events in all tropical seas were recorded between 1979 and 1990. It is feared that bleaching may be a direct result of global warming due to reduction of the ozone layer, but so far there is no conclusive proof.

Dangerous marine animals

Coral reefs are generally safe for normal swimming, wading, and reef-walking activities, but there are a number of potentially harmful animals. Knowledge of these will help to make your reef excursion injury free. Harmful organisms can be divided into two major categories: biters and stingers.

Biters (and nippers) - first and foremost in this category are sharks. There are many types of sharks, but only a few of the reef species are dangerous, including the Tiger, Grey Reef, and Silvertip. Even these dangerous sharks are normally placid and will not attack unless provoked or attracted with dead or struggling fishes. There are a number of smaller reef fishes, which do not pose a direct threat, but can inflict painful bites if handled carelessly. For example, barracudas, razorfishes (a type of wrasse, page 326), puffers, and triggerfishes are notorious in this respect. Any large fish with obvious teeth should be handled with care.

Sea snakes possess venomous fangs, but generally do not pose a threat unless handled. Fatalities among fishermen who encounter snakes in their nets are not uncommon in southeast Asia. Octopuses have a set of horny teeth that can inflict painful bites. Under no circumstance should the Blue-ring octopus be handled as it has a highly venomous bite that can prove fatal(page 208).

Crustaceans with large nippers should be either avoided or at least handled with care. Obviously, the larger the animal, the greater the threat. Species such as the coconut crab (page 150) can easily sever a finger or worse.

Stingers - Any sort of spiny creature is a potential stinger. Virtually any fish with rigid fin spines can inflict painful wounds if carelessly handled. Among the most dangerous category of stingers are fishes that have venomous spines, including stingrays, catfishes, scorpionfishes, and rabbitfishes. The deadly Stonefish (page 269), a type of scorpionfish is among the most poisonous of all animals.

Cnidarians (formerly known as coelenterates) are the best known group of invertebrate stingers. They can penetrate the skin, often with very painful results, by means of a battery of microscopic, venomous darts known as nematocysts. Potentially the most dangerous member of this group is the Box jellyfish (page 46), which invades northern Australian beaches during the summer. Their sting causes excruciating pain and may be fatal. Other cnidarian stingers include jellyfish, Portuguese-man-of-war, hydrozoans, fire coral, and sea anemones.

Most mollusc shells can be safely handled, some cone shells including *Conus aulicus, C. catus, C. geographicus, C. marmoreus, C. omaria, C.striatus, C. textile,* and *C. tulipa* possess a miniature harpoon apparatus that delivers a highly venomous sting that is potentially fatal. Holding these shells by the large end is not entirely safe as the stinger is attached to an extendible proboscis.

Introduction

Sea urchins and the Crown-of-thorns starfish are venomous echinoderms that have obviously dangerous spines and contact should be avoided. Likewise, contact with bristle worms can cause intense itching or burning that may persist for a week or more.

Treatment - It is beyond the scope of this book to provide detailed information on first aid treatment. As a general rule any wound resulting in severe pain is potentially toxic and a physician should be consulted as soon as possible. It is particularly important to seek prompt medical attention in the case of wounds by cone shells, stonefish, lionfish (*Pterois* and *Dendrochirus*), Blue-ring octopus, Box jellyfish, and sea snakes.

For all toxic fish spine stings the recommended first aid procedure is to immerse the wound in hot water (as hot as bearable), repeating until the pain subsides. The protein base of the toxin is denatured by heat and relief is sometimes immediate. Cnidarian stings are effectively treated by applying an Australian commercial product known as "Stingose". Other alternatives are alcohol, methylated spirits, or a local anesthetic ointment such as Xylocaine. Prevention is always the best treatment for cnidarian stings and coral cuts. Cover exposed hands and feet with gloves and wool socks. Wetsuits offer excellent body protection and there is now a wide range of colorful, inexpensive full-body Lycra suits available.

The fin spines of the Indian Ocean firefish, *Pterois milesi* are highly venomous.

The venomous Crown-of-Thorns starfish feeds on live corals and in turn is eaten by the Triton Trumpet shell.

Contact with Fire coral, *Millepora* sp., should be avoided unless gloves are worn.

Chapter 1

Marine Plants
The Reef's Energy Food

Plants are the unheralded heroes of the sea. Without them all forms of marine life simply would not exist. They are the reef's primary producers, converting sunlight and dissolved nutrients into energy-rich organic compounds. Plants provide nutrition for a multitude of microorganisms, as well as numerous larger animals, particularly molluscs, crustaceans, and fishes. These in turn are devoured by larger predators. Plants, therefore, are the basic element of a very complex food web that involves all of the reef's living organisms.

There are two major types of marine plants. Seaweeds or algae are by far the most abundant. They have a simplified, primitive structure compared to the higher plants. In contrast to seagrasses, the other major category, they lack true leaves, stems, and roots. seagrasses, on the other hand, are structurally similar to many land plants, possessing both flowers and fruits, and setting seeds.

Types of seaweed

It is simple to recognize most reef seaweeds on the basis of color, although there are some confusing exceptions. Scientists utilize this same classification scheme in dividing seaweeds into four divisions...red, brown, green, and blue-green.

Blue-green algae is the most primitive type and frequently has the appearance of a crusty blackish slime covering rocks of the splash zone, just above the high-tide line along rocky shores.

Seaweeds are well represented on coral reefs and may occur in shallow tide pools as well as deeper sections of the reef accessible only by SCUBA diving. Reds, browns, and greens are extremely variable in shape. Some types are branching, leaf-like, or bushy. Others form sponge-like encrustations on rocky surfaces. Still others are impregnated with calcium carbonate and have a brittle texture. Red calcareous algae are very common in the intertidal zone or on shallow reefs exposed to strong wave action. They form a coating on the rocky surface that has the appearance of pink or red paint. The calcareous *Halimeda* resembles a rounded, green wafer. Its dead "skeleton" forms thin chips that form a major type of bottom sediment on many reefs.

Brown algae are best represented in temperate latitudes where they form extensive kelp forests. *Sargassum* and *Turbinaria* are among the best known tropical forms. *Sargassum* weed often occurs in extensive beds close to coral reefs. It is constantly lashed by waves and storms, resulting in clumps being detached. Large floating rafts of this plant are sometimes seen far out to sea beyond the sight of land. If you are lucky enough to find a raft, even a small one, it is well worth exploring with a mask and snorkel. They frequently teem with life. Crabs, shrimps, tiny molluscs and juvenile fishes are particularly abundant.

◀ Mangroves and coral at Madang, Papua New Guinea.

The Sargassum anglerfish (page 264) is one of the most intriguing members of the raft community. It is a voracious predator whose coloration blends in perfectly with the surrounding weed.

Besides the already mentioned *Halimeda*, other green algae that are frequently noticed on coral reefs are Sea Lettuce (*Ulva*) and Sea Grapes (*Caulerpa*). *Ulva* is sometimes indicative of pollution as it thrives in water that is enriched by organic wastes. Unlike the reds and browns, green algae are also extremely common in freshwater.

Seagrasses

Seagrasses grow in small clumps amongst coral reefs or in vast meadows in adjacent areas. These meadows are frequently composed of several species as well as various algae that may grow as epiphytes (ie. on the surface of the seagrasses). They are extremely productive, more so than a comparable area of agricultural land. In contrast to seaweeds, relatively few animals consume seagrasses. These include sea urchins, some molluscs, turtles, and dugongs.

Mangroves

Strictly speaking, mangroves are not a common element of coral reef habitats. However, they are sometimes situated in close proximity. The mangrove habitat is a distinct ecosystem that is well worth exploring. The submerged roots and trunks, and aerial forest provides a home for a wealth of diverse organisms. Be warned though, this also includes mosquitoes and sand flies. Be sure and take proper dress precautions and plenty of insect repellent along if you intend to enjoy your outing.

Embryonic root-stems and fruits of *Rhizophora stylosa*, a commom mangrove of tropical shores.

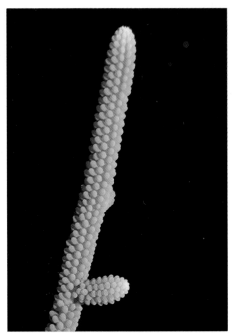

Caulerpa ethelae, 7 cm.

Sea grapes, *Caulerpa racemosa*, 5 cm height.

Sea grapes, *Caulerpa racemosa*, 20 cm height.

Sea grapes, *Caulerpa racemosa*, 5 cm height.

Caulerpa serrulata, 7 cm width.

Caulerpa taxifola, 5 cm height.

Caulerpa webbiana.

Turtle weed, *Chlorodesmis fastigiata.*

Sponge weed, *Ceratodictyon spongiosum,*
20 cm height.

Button weed, *Dictyosphaeria versluysii,*
15 cm width.

Dictyosphaeria sp., 4 cm each.

Coralline alga, *Halimeda capiosa,* clump
width 30 cm.

Coralline alga, *Halimeda cylindracea,* clump
width 15 cm.

Coralline alga, *Halimeda discoidea,* clump
width 12 cm.

Coralline alga, *Halimeda macroloba,* clump
width 12 cm.

Coralline alga, *Halimeda micronesica*,
clump width 30 cm.

Coralline alga, *Halimeda opuntia*, clump
width 15 cm.

Caterpillar weed, *Neomeris annulata*,
3 cm height.

Tydemania expeditionis, 12 cm.

Udotea sp.. 5 cm.

Sea lettuce, *Ulva* sp., 10 cm.

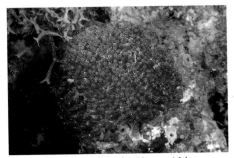

Valonia aegagropila., 10 cm width.

Sailor's eyeball, *Valonia ventricosa*, 6 cm.

Spikeweed, *Actinotrichia fragilis*, 6cm width.

Spikeweed, *Actinotrichia fragilis*, clump width 25 cm.

Dictyota sp., clump width 15 cm.

Dictyota sp., clump width 10 cm..

Dictyota sp., clump width 20 cm.

Branching red alga, possibly *Amphiroa foliacea*, 5 cm.

Galaxaura marginata, clump width 15 cm.

Fauchea peltata, 3 cm.

Halymenia durvillaei, clump width 30 cm.

Halymenia sp., clump width 20 cm.

Coralline red alga, *Haliptilon* sp., clump width 20 cm.

Red filamentous alga, *Lyngbya bouillonii*.

Coralline red alga, possibly *Lithothamnion prolifer*.

Coralline red alga, probably *Neogoniolithon brassica*.

Unidentified coralline red alga.

Red alga, possibly *Nemastoma* sp., 10 cm height.

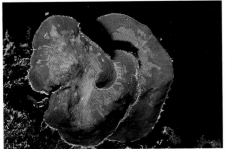

Crustose red alga, *Peyssonnelia* sp., 6 cm width.

Branching red alga, possibly *Rhodymenia* sp., 20 cm width.

Jellyweed, *Titanophora weberae*, 20 cm height.

Zellera tawallina, clump width 30 cm.

Funnelweed, *Padina gymnospora*, 10 cm width.

Sargassum sp., a common tropical seaweed.

Turbinweed, *Turbinaria* sp., 7 cm width.

Unidentified alga, probably a filamentous blue-green.

Seagrass, *Cymodocea serrulata*, 15 cm height.

Seagrass, *Enhalus acoroides*, 80 cm height.

Seagrass, *Halodule pinifolia*?, 10 cm height.

Seagrass, *Halophila ovalis*, 5 cm height.

Seagrass, *Syringodium isoetifolium*, 25 cm height.

Mangrove (*Rhizophora*) and coral (*Porites*) habitat.

Roots of the mangrove tree *Rhizophora stylosa*.

Mangrove tree, *Sonneratia caseolaris*.

Chapter 2

Foraminiferida
Unappreciated Reef Builders

This group contains tiny, rather inconspicuous single-celled animals belonging to the Phylum Sarcomastigophora. They are extremely common on coral reefs, but easily over-looked. The structure of these organisms, commonly known as forams, is extremely simple. They are virtually a blob of jelly-like protoplasm within a shell of calcium carbonate. There is also an outer layer of protoplasm with projections known as pseudopods. These can be expanded and contracted to provide a very slow form of locomotion. They are also used for feeding, waste expulsion, and gas exchange. Forams have a symbiotic alga living within their protoplasm, which manufactures vital nutrients. These simple creatures also feed on a variety of microscopic organisms including larvae and eggs.

Forams are either free living or may be attached to other organisms, particularly various types of algae and seagrasses. There are also pelagic species that float in the open sea. In some areas they occur in plague proportions that seem to build up very quickly. For example, we found huge numbers of the foram *Marginopora vertebralis* at a small offshore is-let near Madang, Papua New Guinea in 1993. In spite of numerous dives over several years at this locality we had never seen it previously.

There are many species of forams and each has a distinctive shell that is composed of one or more chambers. The empty shells of dead forams are a major contributor to bottom sediments in many areas and there-fore play an important role in the reef-building process. We recently visited a beach in East Bali that was composed of nearly 100 percent forams. It has been esti-mated that about 50 percent of the Earth's calcareous sedimentary rock formed on sea bottoms originates from the shells of these animals.

Marginopora vertebralis, each disc
1 cm diameter.

◀ Sea grapes, *Caulerpa racemosa* (green alga).

Chapter 3

Sponges
Simple, but Effective

Sponges have the least complex body structure of all multi-celled creatures. A typical sponge is composed of an outer layer of tissue, the cortex, and a fibrous inner layer impregnated with numerous glass-like slivers of silica or calcium carbonate. The outer surface is riddled with small openings (often microscopic) called ostia. These join a complex network of internal canals, through which water circulates. The canals frequently empty into one or more large conduits that exit via an osicule, a large opening on the external surface of the sponge. There is no denying that this very simple body plan is effective. It has remained little changed since Devonian times (approximately 450 million years ago) when sponges were the dominant form of life in shallow seas.

Nature's vacuum cleaners

Sponges are extremely efficient filter feeders. The inner canals are lined with special feeding cells known as choanocytes. Each cell is equipped with a thread-like tail (cilia) that projects into the canal. Vigorous movement of these tails create a current that moves food-laden water through the sponge. This movement also creates a vacuum effect, drawing the surrounding water into the ostia. A typical sponge pumps water equal to 4-5 times its own volume every minute. For a football-sized sponge this translates to several thousand liters each day. Sponges can filter the smallest of microscopic organisms. They are particularly efficient in filtering bacteria, a major source of nutrition.

Because of their predilection for bacteria and other organic debris sponges are often abundant and robust at the entrance of harbors or off river mouths. They are also prominent in areas exposed to vigorous currents which greatly facilitates the movement of water into the feeding canals.

Numerous sponges found on coral reefs are impregnated with the living tissue of blue-green algae. This symbiotic relationship is similar to that found between different types of algae and various corals, molluscs, and ascidians. The algal cells carry on photosynthetic activities and leak a significant amount of energy-rich sugar compounds directly into the sponge tissue. In some types of sponge the algae may supply nearly 100 percent of the nutritional requirements.

An estimated 10,000 species of sponges are known. All except one family of freshwater species are found in the sea. They occur in a wide range of habitats, from deep oceanic trenches to shallow tide pools. However, the greatest diversity is found on shallow tropical seas. The identification of tropical species is frequently difficult. Even high quality photographs may be of little use as we discovered when consulting several specialists. The problem lies in the extremely variable appearance that a single species of sponge assumes according to environmental factors. For example, a particular species found in a protected lagoon may exhibit an entirely different shape

◀ *Nara nematifera*, 12 cm, photographed on the Great Barrier Reef, Australia.

and color than the same species situated in an area of strong current on the outer reef. Species determination usually relies on the microscopic examination of the internal skeletal elements, the spicules.

Classification and characteristics

Nearly all living sponges belong to a group (suborder) known as the Demospongiae. They characteristically have spicules composed of silica. In many species the spicules are in the shape of needle-like rods with pointed ends. Other species have multi-pronged, star-like clusters of needles, and a few have an anchor-shaped arrangement. A relatively small number of species have spicules composed of calcium carbonate. One of these, the living fossil sponge (*Astrosclera willeyana*) is a spherical organism consisting of a nearly solid limestone skeleton, covered by a thin outer layer of living tissue. This species is sometimes seen in caves or under ledges. Sponges of the suborder Calcarea also possess spicules of calcium carbonate. They are frequently small (to about 10cm in height), tubular forms that can be seen on the underside of rocks and coral slabs on shallow reefs.

Sponge partners

Sponges sometimes host an array of other organisms, including various crabs, shrimps, worms, sea cucumbers, feather stars, and fishes. Feather stars and small gobiid fishes use the sponge to gain access to plankton-rich currents passing above. Small synaptid sea cucumbers are one of the most obvious commensals seen on sponges. Large barrel sponges and certain fan sponges may be literally covered with hundreds of these organisms. The sea cucumbers feed on the larger organic debris that accumulates on the outer surface (see page 247).

Sponge Identification

Sponges are very difficult to identify from photographs. Positive identification is largely dependent on the examination of a specimen sample. The experts we consulted were therefore hesitant in providing scientific names for some species. These uncertain identifications are indicated with a question mark.

Calcareous sponge,
Pericharax heteroraphis
(Leucettida), 30 cm.

Calcareous sponge, *Pericharax heteroraphis* (Leucettida), 30 cm.

Astrosclera willeyana (Agelasida, Agelasidae), 3 cm.

Aplysina sp. (Verongida, Aplysinidae), 25 cm.

Asteropus sarassinorum (Astrophorida, Coppatiidae), 30 cm.

Jaspis stellifera (Astrophorida, Coppatiidae), 80 cm.

Jaspis sp. (Astrophorida, Coppatiidae), 10 cm.

Stylotella aurantium (Halichondrida, Halichondriidae), 15 cm.

Phakellia aruensis
(Axinellida, Axinellidae), 50 cm.

Phakellia flabellata
(Axinellida, Axinellidae), 30 cm.

Acanthella cavernosa
(Axinellida, Axinellidae), 15 cm.

Thalysias vulpina
(Poecilosclerida, Microcionidae), 40cm

Cribrochalina sp.
(Haplosclerida, Niphatidae)

Acanthella klethra (Axinellida, Axinellidae), 20 cm.

Reniochalina stalagmitis (Axinellida, Axinellidae), 15 cm.

Sponges

Aplysilla? sp.
(Dendroceratida, Aplysillidae), 30 cm.

Carteriospongia sp.
(Dictyoceratida, Spongiidae), 35 cm.

Dysidea sp.
(Dictyoceratida, Dysideidae), 30 cm.

Dysidea sp. (Dictyoceratida, Dysideidae), 10 cm.

Hyattella intestinalis
(Dictyoceratida, Spongiidae), 30 cm.

Strepsichordaia lendenfeldi
(Dictyoceratida, Spongiidae), 30 cm.

Phyllospongia lamellosa (Dictyoceratida,
Spongiidae), 35 cm.

Aaptos suberitoides (Hadromerida, Tethyidae),
colony width 40 cm.

Spirastrella vagabunda (Hadromerida,
Spirastrellidae), 30 cm.

Unidentified sponge, Order Hadromerida, 5 cm.

Epipolasis suluensis? (Halichondrida,
Halichondriidae), 8 cm.

Halichondria cartilaginea (Halichondrida,
Halichondriidae), 35 cm.

Stylotella aurantium (Halichondrida,
Halichondriidae), 35 cm.

Callyspongia muricina (Haplosclerida,
Callyspongiidae), 50 cm.

Callyspongia pseudoreticulata
(Haplosclerida, Callyspongiidae), 50 cm.

Callyspongia sp.
(Haplosclerida, Callyspongiidae), 30 cm.

Cribrochalina olemda
(Haplosclerida, Niphatidae), 40 cm.

Niphates sp.
(Haplosclerida, Niphatidae), 30 cm.

Cribrochalina olemda
(Haplosclerida, Niphatidae), 40 cm.

Callyspongia sp.
(Haplosclerida, Callyspongiidae), 25 cm.

Theonella cylindrica
("Lithistida", Theonellidae), 70 cm.

Gelliodes fibulatus
(Haplosclerida, Niphatidae), 15 cm.

Gelliodes sp.
(Haplosclerida, Niphatidae), 40 cm.

Gelliodes sp.
(Haplosclerida, Niphatidae), 60 cm.

Niphates? sp.
(Haplosclerida, Niphatidae), 12 cm.

Callyspongia sp.
(Haplosclerida, Callyspongiidae), 20 cm.

Gelliodes sp.
(Haplosclerida, Niphatidae), 30 cm.

Callyspongia sp.
(Haplosclerida, Callyspongiidae), 15 cm.

Oceanapia sp.
(Haplosclerida, Oceanapiidae), 30 cm.

Sponges

Oceanapia amboinensis. (Haplosclerida, Oceanapiidae), 40 cm height.

Petrosia sp. (Haplosclerida, Petrosiidae), 50 cm.

Xestospongia exigua (Haplosclerida, Petrosiidae), 40 cm.

Xestospongia exigua? (Haplosclerida, Petrosiidae), 20 cm.

Xestospongia sp. (Haplosclerida, Petrosiidae), 12 cm.

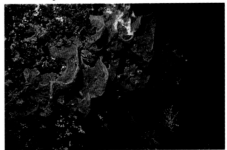

Xestospongia exigua (Haplosclerida, Petrosiidae), 180 cm.

Xestospongia testudinaria (Haplosclerida, Petrosiidae), 70 cm.

Xestospongia testudinaria (Haplosclerida, Petrosiidae), 130 cm.

Xestospongia sp.
(Haplosclerida, Petrosiidae), 50 cm.

Callyspongia sp.
(Haplosclerida, Callyspongiidae), 50 cm.

Plakortis nigra
(Homosclerophorida, Plakinidae), 40cm.

Clathria basilana
(Poecilosclerida, Microcionidae), 7 cm.

Cribrochalina sp.
(Haplosclerida, Niphatidae), 50 cm.

Clathria reinwardti
(Poecilosclerida, Microcionidae), 50 cm.

Clathria reinwardti
(Poecilosclerida, Microcionidae), 60 cm.

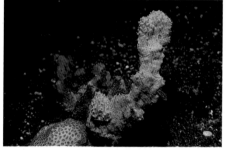

Clathria tuberosa
(Poecilosclerida, Microcionidae), 25 cm.

Clathria sp.
(Poecilosclerida, Microcionidae), 40 cm.

Coelocarteria singaporense
(Poecilosclerida, Coelosphoeridae), 30 cm.

Agelas sp.
(Agelasida, Agelasiidae), 80 cm.

Desmapsamma sp.
(Poecilosclerida, Desmacididae), 30 cm.

Echinodictyum sp.
(Poecilosclerida, Raspailiidae), 50 cm.

Haliclona amboinensis
(Haplosclerida, Chalinidae), 7 cm.

Haliclona amboinensis
(Haplosclerida, Chalinidae), 20 cm.

Haliclona cymiformis
(Haplosclerida Chalinidae), 60 cm.

Haliclona fascigera
(Haplosclerida, Chalinidae), 30 cm.

Auletta sp.
(Axinellida, Axinellidae), 8 cm.

Auletta sp.
(Axinellida, Axinellidae), 12 cm.

Haliclona sp.
(Haplosclerida Chalinidae), 10 cm.

Haliclona sp.
(Haplosclerida, Chalinidae), 7 cm.

Cribrochalina sp.
(Haplosclerida, Niphatidae), 15 cm.

Auletta sp.
(Axinellida, Axinellidae), 30 cm.

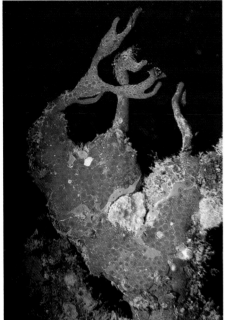

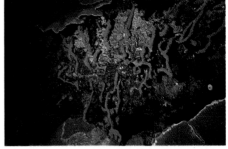

Gelliodes sp.
(Haplosclerida, Niphatidae), 200 cm colony.

Strongylacidon sp.
(Poecilosclerida, Desmacididae), 12 cm.

Crambe ? sp.
(Poecilosclerida, Esperiopsidae), 5 cm.

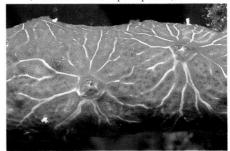

Aka sp.
(Haplosclerida, Niphatidae), 5 cm.

Clathria sp.
(Poecilosclerida, Microcionidae), 5 cm.

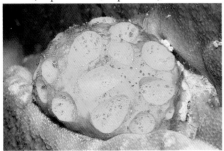

Cinachyra sp.
(Spirophorida, Tetillidae), 10 cm.

Craniella sp.
(Spirophorida, Tetillidae), 12 cm.

Ianthella flabelliformis (Verongida, Ianthellidae), 50 cm.

Ianthella basta
(Verongida, Ianthellidae), 70 cm.

Ianthella basta
(Verongida, Ianthellidae), 100 cm.

Ianthella sp.
(Verongida, Ianthellidae), 70 cm.

Ciocalypta sp.
(Halichondrida, Halichondriidae), 10 cm.

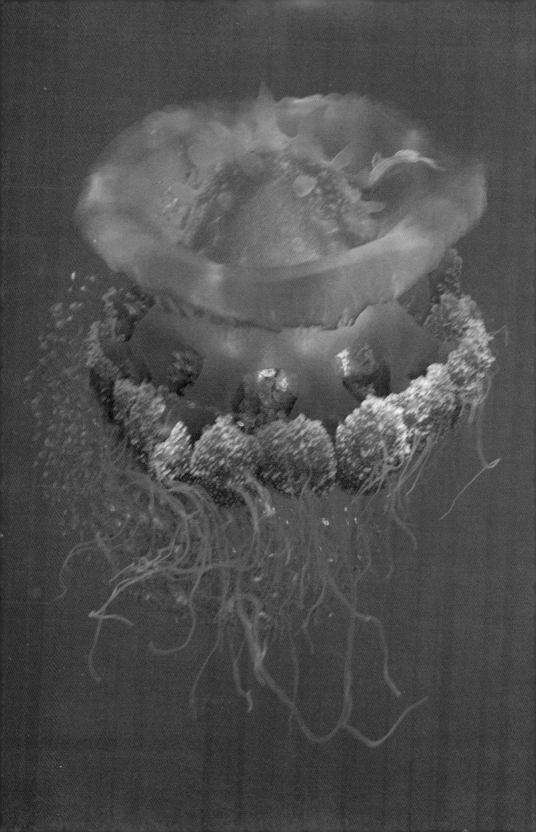

Chapter 4

Jellyfish
Beware of the Stingers

The Phylum Cnidaria (formerly called coelenterates) is a major division of the animal kingdom containing jellyfish, various types of hard and soft coral, and gorgonian sea whips and fans, hydroids, and sea anemones. It is a remarkably diverse group, but there are a few similarities that bind them. First and foremost is the basic body plan. They have a peculiar ciliated larval stage known as a planula. Later in life they transform (metamorphose) into either an attached polyp or a free-swimming medusa. Some jellyfish pass through both of these stages. Basically the medusa and polyp are very similar in their organization, consisting of a soft body with tentacles clustered around a central mouth. In the medusa the mouth and tentacles are usually directed downward, but in polyps they are typically directed upwards or laterally. In addition, the free-swimming medusa (most jellyfish for example) generally occurs solitarily. There are types of solitary corals, but most polyps are occur in colonies.

Spring-loaded darts

The tentacles of jellyfishes and other cnidarians possess specialized stinging cells, the nematocysts. These are microscopic, spring-loaded darts that are extremely sensitive to pressure. When touched, literally hundreds or thousands may be discharged. Normally this mechanism is used to capture prey, ranging in size from small fishes to microscopic plankton. The sting of many jellyfishes is harmless; the nematocysts are unable to penetrate human skin. However, quite a few species are capable of delivering very painful stings and a few can cause death. It is best to avoid contact with all of them, just to be on the safe side.

The jellyfish with the most notorious reputation is the dreaded Box jelly (*Chironex fleckeri*). In Australia it has been responsible for a number of fatalities. Small children are particularly vulnerable. Box jellys are common in inshore areas during the summer months (wet season). Fortunately this species is not usually seen on offshore coral reefs, including the Great Barrier Reef.

The rhizostome jellys have a thick "fluffy" frill between the upper bell and lower tentacles. The central frill underneath actually contains numerous mouths that are particularly efficient for trapping small organisms from the surrounding water. The Upside-down jelly is another unusual type commonly found in sandy areas near reefs. Unlike most jellyfish it is usually seen lying on the bottom with its bushy "mouth-arms" directed upwards. At first glance it is easily mistaken for a sea anemone.

Reef jellys are frequently seen with a compliment of small fishes, often juvenile jacks or trevallies, swimming among the tentacles. The fish utilize the jelly in much the same manner that clownfishes use their anemone hosts. Evidently the fishes are not stung by the jelly and therefore obtain protection from predators during the vulnerable youthful stages of their life cycle. When large enough to fend for themselves the jacks abandon their host.

◄ Crown jellyfish, *Cephea* sp, 50 cm disc.

Papuan jellyfish, *Mastigias papua* (Mastigiidae),
15 cm disc diameter.

Hydrozoan medusa, *Aequorea pensilis*
(Aequoreidae), 12 cm disc diameter.

Cigar jellyfish, *Olindias phosphorica*
(Olindiidae), 6 cm.

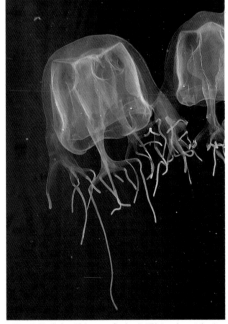

Box jellyfish, *Chironex fleckeri* (Chirodropidae),
45 cm length.

Portugese man-of-war, *Physalia physalis*
(Physaliidae), 8 cm.

Jellyfish *Thysanostoma thysanura* (Order Rhizostomeae), 25 cm length.

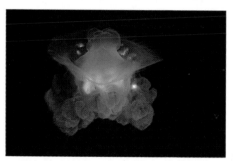

Jellyfish, *Cephea cephea* (Cepheidae), 30 cm length.

Lion's-mane jellyfish, *Cyanea capillata* (Cyaneidae), 40 cm disc diameter.

Jellyfish, *Thystanostoma flagellatum* (Thysanostomatidae), 25 cm length.

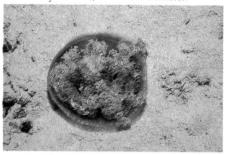

Upside-down jellyfish, *Cassiopea andromeda* (Cassiopeidae), 7 cm disc diameter.

Chapter 5

Hydrozoans
Pests in Paradise

A holiday excursion to the tropics is always a pleasurable experience, but there can be plenty of minor irritations. If somehow we could get rid of mosquitoes and sandflys our evenings would be infinitely more enjoyable. These airborne pests certainly have an underwater equivalent in the form of hydroids (Class Hydroza). Uncomfortable stings received from these common creatures have caused many a sleepless night. But how can they be avoided? Prevention is definitely the best cure. Cover up all exposed surfaces. This means wearing either a wetsuit or lycra suit, and gloves are a must. Even with these precautions stings are common to the wrist and ankle areas.

Jellyfish relatives

Hydrozoans are related to jellyfish and corals; all belong to the Phylum Cnidaria. The stings of these animals are caused by nematocysts (see discussion in Chapter 5). Hydroids are the most common form of hydrozoan occurring on coral reefs. In many areas these feathery, plant-shaped animals literally coat the reef's surface. Fire coral (*Millipora*) is another common hydrozoan. From outward appearances it is easily mistaken for a hard (scleractinian) coral. The Portuguese Man-of-War is also a type of hydrozoan. Although occasionally seen at the surface on coral reefs, it is more common in the open sea or washed up on beaches (see page 46).

Hydroids are colonial animals. Each colony has the appearance of a feather, with a central stalk and many side branches. Tiny polyps with characteristic cnidarian tentacles occur on the branches. Some polyps are specialized for feeding and armed with nematocysts. Others function as reproductive organs. The feeding polyps sieve the passing current for microscopic organisms and organic debris. Food is shared among the polyps by an interconnecting digestive tube.

Fire corals also have a colonial structure. They assume a wide variety of growth forms, similar to that seen in scleractinian corals. These include branching colonies, encrusting growths, and vertical plates. Fire corals and other types of hydrozoans that secrete a hard limestone skeleton are generally referred to as hydrocorals. This group also includes the beautiful, delicately branched lace corals (*Distichopora* and *Stylaster*) that are common under ledges or on the walls and ceilings of caves.

Hydroids generally reproduce by sexual means. Tiny medusae form on the branches. These eventually break off and become free-swimming. They produce either eggs or sperm that are released in the surrounding waters. Fertilized eggs hatch into planula larvae that eventually attach to the reef's surface and grow into a new branching colony.

◀ Stinging hydrozan, *Aglaophenia cupressina*, 35 cm height.

Stinging hydrozan, *Aglaophenia cupressina*, 35 cm height.

Aglaophenia cupressina, 20 cm height.

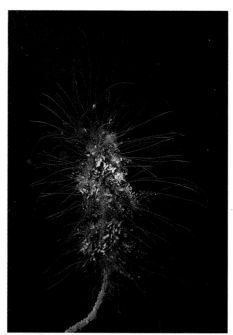

Halocordyle disticha (Halocordylidae), 10 cm.

Plumularia? sp. (Plumulariidae), 10 cm height.

Lytocarpus philippinus (Plumulariidae), 30 cm height.

Lytocarpus phoenicus (Plumulariidae), 15 cm height.

Plumularia sp. (Plumulariidae), 15 cm height.

Unidentified species, possibly *Gymnagium* or *Aglaophenia* (Plumulariidae), 8 cm height.

Sertularia? sp. (Sertulariidae), 60 cm height.

Fire coral, *Millepora* sp., 25 cm height.

Fire coral, *Millepora* sp.

Fire coral, *Millepora dichotoma*? (Milleporidae).

Fire coral, *Millepora tenella* (Milleporidae).

Encrusting fire coral, *Millepora* sp. (Milleporidae).

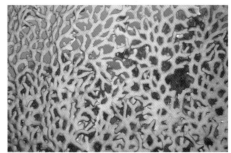

Fire coral, *Millepora* sp. (Milleporidae), 25 cm width.

Lace coral, *Distichopora violacea* (Stylasteridae), 10 cm.

Lace coral, *Distichopora* sp. (Stylasteridae), 10 cm.

Lace coral, *Stylaster* sp. (Stylasteridae), 12 cm.

Lace coral, *Stylaster* sp. (Stylasteridae), 25 cm.

Chapter 6

Sea Anemones
Kingdom and Castle of the Clownfish

There are many types of anemones found on coral reefs, but relatively few are readily visible. Most are well hidden in cracks and crevices, or underneath rocks and dead coral slabs. The most conspicuous types are those found with the colorful clownfishes (see page 308). Most fishes would be stung by the anemone, but clownfishes have a special mucus coating which prevents the anemone from stinging them.

Ten species of clownfish anemones are known. They range in size from just a few centimeters in width to over a metre. In some the tentacles are short and knobby, but others have long, slender ones. The basic body plan of an anemone is very simple consisting of a hollow tube with muscular walls that is closed at both ends. Actually the hollow center of the tube has a number of thin-walled partitions. Cut open in cross section it looks like a wheel with spokes. These partitions serve to increase the digestive area and enhance various metabolic processes including respiration and excretion.

Anemone anatomy

Several main body regions are apparent when viewing an anemone. The crown of tentacles is frequently the most obvious. Tentacles vary in number according to the type of anemone, but in every case they surround the mouth and function in obtaining food. The upper surface from which the tentacles arise is called the oral disc. The sides of the cylindrical or tubular body is known as the column. It is frequently smooth, but sometimes has wart-like bumps, which are helpful in recognizing some species. The bottom of the anemone is called the pedal disc. It is usually attached to a hard surface, most often rock, rubble, or dead coral, which may be buried under the sand.

The tentacles contain hundreds of microscopic stinging cells or nematocysts. These are used for capturing food items or in repelling predators, such as butterflyfishes. Anemones normally feed on planktonic plants and animals. The clownfish anemones can be safely handled because the nematocysts are too tiny to penetrate the skin. However, if you have any cuts or scratches a stinging sensation may be experienced.

Just an overgrown coral

Anemones are closely related to the reef-building hard corals. Both are members of the Class Anthozoa within the Phylum Cnidaria. Structurally they are very similar. Essentially an anemone is nothing more than an overgrown coral polyp that lacks a hard skeleton. As in many types of coral polyps the anemone's tentacles contain a special type of alga known as zooxanthellae. It utilizes sunlight and carbon dioxide to produce high-energy substances that are leaked to the host anemones, thus providing an important dietary supplement. Because of their relationship with zooxanthellae, most of the large anemones achieve maximum growth in shallow, sun-lit waters. The alga is also responsible for imparting a greenish or brown hue to the tentacles.

◄ Magnificent sea anemone, *Heteractis magnifica*, Flores, Indonesia.

Anemones can multiply by means of fragmentation. Sexual reproduction also occurs. Sexes are generally separate. Eggs and sperm are released in open water and a free-swimming larva, the planula, emerges from the fertilized egg. Very little is known about the early life history of the clownfish anemones. It is certain, however, that very few of the larvae survive. This is evident from the extreme rarity of small anemones seen on reefs. Once settled in a favorable location, anemones rarely move, although they are capable of very slow, sliding-type movement with the pedal disc. Large anemones are occasionally seen drifting in open water, apparently having been dislodged by storms. The large clownfish anemones appear to have a considerable lifespan, sometimes exceeding 100 years. Because of their poor reproductive success and long lifespan it is extremely important to discourage the collection of these anemones. Many are harvested each year in the Philippines, Indonesia, and other areas for the aquarium trade.

Cerianthids, Coralliomorpharians, and Zooanthideans

Another type of anemone commonly seen on sandy bottoms near reefs is the cerianthid or tube anemone (belonging to the Order Ceriantharia). They have a double row of long, graceful tentacles that are fully extended when the current is running. Cerianthids differ from other anemones in having a horny or leathery tube at the base into which they can withdraw for protection.

The Order Coralliomorpharia contains anemone-like animals that are found either as solitary individuals or in small to very large colonies that may carpet extensive sections of reef. *Amplexidiscus fenestrafer* (page 61) is the largest known species. It is capable of capturing and consuming small fishes.

Members of the Order Zooanthidea are mainly colonial forms whose polyps resemble small anemones. At first some colonies are easily mistaken for true corals, but instead of having a hard, calcareous skeleton, the polyps are embedded in a semi-soft matrix known as the mesogloea. Many species have the ability to incorporate bottom sediments into the mesogloea as they grow, thus giving added support and protection for the polyps. Zooanthideans can reproduce asexually or may spawn in a fashion similar to that of hard corals (see Chapter 7).

Gigantic sea anemone,
Stichodactyla gigantea,
(Stichodactylidae),
35 cm width.

Branching anemone, *Actinodendron arboreum*
(Actinodendronidae), 30 cm width.

Branching anemone, *Actinodendron arboreum*
(Actinodendronidae), 30 cm width.

Branching anemone, *Actinodendron plumosum*
(Actinodendronidae), 25 cm height.

Branching anemone, *Actinodendron* sp.
(Actinodendronidae), 25 cm height.

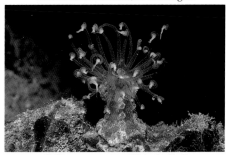

Branching anemone, *Actinostephanus haeckeli*
(Actinodendronidae), 40 cm width.

Solitary anemone, *Alicia rhadina*?
(Aliciidae), 12 cm height.

Colonial anemone, *Amphianthus* sp.
(Hormathiidae), each 5 cm.

Colonial anemone, *Amphianthus* sp.
(Hormathiidae), each 4 cm.

Colonial anemone, *Amphianthus* sp.
(Hormathiidae), each 5 cm.

Sea anemone, possibly *Dofleinia armata*,
5 cm disc width.

Colonial anemone, *Nemanthus*? sp.
(Nemanthidae), 2 cm disc width.

Sea anemone, *Telmatactis* sp. (Isophellidae),
6 cm disc width.

Adhesive sea anemone, *Cryptodendrum
adhaesivum* (Thalassianthidae), 70 cm disc width.

Sea anemone, *Heterodactyla hemprichii*
(Thalassianthidae), 15 cm disc width.

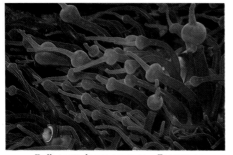

Bulb-tentacle sea anemone, *Entacmaea
quadricolor* (Actiniidae), tentacle length 10 cm.

Beaded sea anemone, *Heteractis aurora*
(Stichodactylidae), 28 cm disc width.

Leathery sea anemone, *Heteractis crispa*
(Stichodactylidae), 50 cm disc width.

Magnificent sea anemone, *Heteractis magnifica*
(Stichodactylidae), 40 cm disc width.

Delicate sea anemone, *Heteractis malu*
(Stichodactylidae), 12 cm disc width.

Corkscrew tentacle sea anemone, *Macrodactyla
doreensis* (Actiniidae), 35 cm disc width.

Gigantic sea anemone, *Stichodactyla gigantea*
(Stichodactylidae), 40 cm disc width.

Haddon's sea anemone, *Stichodactyla haddoni*
(Stichodactylidae), 40 cm disc width.

Mertens' sea anemone, *Stichodactyla mertensii*
(Stichodactylidae), 60 cm disc width.

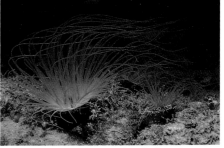

Tube anemone, unidentified species
(Ceranthidae), 30 cm height.

Anemones – Family Cerianthidae

Tube Anemone, unidentified species, 30 cm height.

Tube anemone, unidentified species, 15 cm height.

Corallimorpharian, *Amplexidiscus fenestrafer*, 30 cm width.

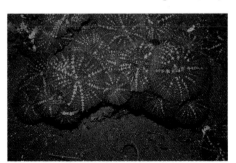

Corallimorpharian, *Discosoma* sp.,
10 cm width each.

Corallimorpharian, *Discosoma* sp.,
colony width 8 cm.

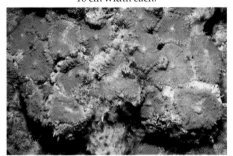

Corallimorpharian, *Discosoma* sp.,
4 cm width each.

Corallimorpharian, *Discosoma* sp.,
10 cm width each.

Corallimorpharian, *Amplexidiscus fenestrafer*, 30 cm width each.

Corallimorpharian, *Discosoma* sp., 30 cm width.

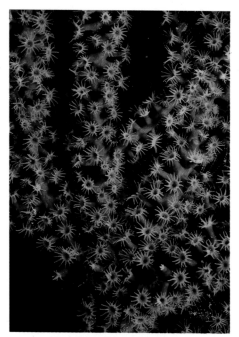

Zoantharian, *Parazoanthus* sp.,
colony width 8 cm.

Zoantharian, *Parazoanthus*? sp.,
colony height 12 cm.

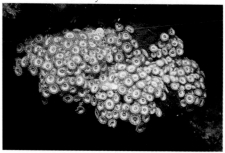

Zoantharian, *Protopalythoa* sp., colony width 20 cm.

Zoantharian, *Protopalythoa* sp., colony width 8 cm.

Zoantharian, *Palythoa* sp., colony width 20 cm.

Zoantharian, *Palythoa* sp. with polyps retracted,
colony width 12 cm.

Chapter 7

Corals
The Reef's Crowning Glory

Millions upon millions of tiny coral polyps are the life blood of the reef. The skeletons they secrete impart an obvious esthetic quality, but this beauty is far more than skin deep. Skeletons deposited by countless generations of coral polyps form the solid limestone foundation or platform on which the reef flourishes. Experimental drilling samples indicate that some reef platforms in the Indo-Pacific region are hundreds of meters thick.

This chapter covers the hard or stony corals, known as scleractinians. Approximately 500 species are known from the Indo-Pacific. The richest area is centered around Australia and Indonesia where about 70 percent of the species are found. Many corals have broad distribution patterns that extend from the Red Sea and East Africa to islands of the Central Pacific. Although there are solitary types such as the mushroom corals (Fungiidae), the vast majority of species are colonial forms. In the latter category the members of the genus *Acropora*, frequently referred to as table corals and staghorn corals, are especially abundant.

An individual coral polyp consists of a fleshy sack topped with a ring of tentacles around a central mouth opening. It sits in a limestone skeletal case, which is actually secreted by the polyp. Members of the colony are linked by living tissue. Therefore nutrients captured by a section of the colony can be shared around. Many corals have brownish colored, unicellular algae (zooxanthellae) living within the tissues of the polyps. They are called hermatypic corals.

The algae use sunlight and carbon dioxide to produce carbon enriched organic compounds. These in turn are leaked to the polyp and may provide as much as 98 percent of its nutritional requirements. Hermatypic corals typically grow in clear, sunlit waters, but many are also found in relatively low light levels. They are slower growing and thus have reduced nutritional needs. The diet may be supplemented by absorbing dissolved nutrients directly from the water, or by feeding on bacteria and organic debris. Another group, the ahermatypic corals, do not have zooanthellae. They rely on capturing prey with their stinging cells. Much of the food consists of microorganisms, but some corals can capture worms, urchins, and even fishes.

Coral identification

Major groups (families and often genera) of corals can be readily identified in the field, but recognition of individual species may be difficult for all but a trained specialist. Species are generally identified on the basis of their skeletal characteristics. Coral experts collect small samples of the colony then prepare the specimen by washing out the polyps and bleaching the skeleton. It may be necessary to examine the prepared skeleton under a microscope to confirm the identification. Our aim in this chapter is to present broad coverage that includes many of the common corals found in shallow water as well as a few of the rarer and deep-dwelling species.

The difficulties of coral identification are often compounded by a variety of growth forms

◀ Rich coral growth on the Great Barrier Reef, Australia

and colors present within a single species. Both structure and color are strongly influenced by environmental factors. For example, a species may have very robust, globular branches when found in shallow, wave-affected locations. However, when it occurs in deeper, more sheltered conditions, the branches will tend to be thinner, with an overall delicate appearance. Similarly, some corals, particularly *Acropora*, may assume a tabular form in some situations, and a finger-like structure in others. Color of an individual species can vary greatly according to its exposure to sunlight. In shallow water the zooxanthellae may impart strong shades of brown, green, or yellow. These colors tend to fade with increasing depth and resultant decrease of light. We often see eye-catching shades of red, pink and blue exhibited by corals living in shallow water. Sometimes only the branch tips or zone of new growth is brightly colored.

Hidden polyps

The majority of corals seen during the day keep their polyps retracted. We normally see them only as skeletal formations unless diving at night. The bright orange dendrophylliid corals *(Dendrophyllia* and *Tubastraea)* that grow in caves and on shipwrecks are especially spectacular. Two types of poritid corals, members of the genera *Alveopora* and *Goniopora* are among the minority that do show their polyps during daylight hours. The polyps have long slender stalks tipped with beautiful, flower-like tentacles. The hard skeleton of the colony may be completely obscured by the waving polyps. At first glance Bubble corals *(Plerogyra* and *Physogyra)* also appear to expose their fleshy tentacles during the day. However, these are actually grape-like, water-filled vesicles that protects the delicate hidden polyps.

Reproduction

Growth of a coral colony is achieved by asexual multiplication. The existing polyps simply divide to form new ones. This results in relatively rapid growth. The fastest growing staghorn corals may add as much as 15 cm per year to their branching tips. Massive boulder type *Porites* coral grows at about half this rate, but colonies can reach gargantuan heights of nearly three meters. Formations such as this may be nearly 1000 years old! However, it must be remembered that only the youthful, outer layer is actually alive. Corals also reproduce sexually. Polyps are either hermaphroditic (both sexes present) or produce either eggs or sperm. Nature has devised a clever method to maximize the chances of fertilization. Mass coral spawning occurs mainly on a few nights of the year. This phenomenon has been best studied on the Great Barrier Reef. At this location the event occurs shortly after the full moon in November. It starts one or two nights after the full moon and continues for several days, with most of the action on the fourth, fifth or sixth night. Night dives at this time are a memorable experience. Millions of eggs are liberated and lazily float to the surface. Its like being in the midst of an upside down snowstorm. The fertilized eggs hatch into planula larvae and lead a planktonic life until settling onto the reef to begin a new colony.

Enemies

Predation of eggs and larvae by the reef's numerous plankton feeders is extremely heavy. Only a tiny percentage of larvae are able to find a suitable bare rock surface to settle on. Even fully mature coral colonies are ravaged by a variety of predators. These include the notorious Crown-of-thorns starfish, coral eating molluscs called drupes, fishes, and coral-burrowing worms and molluscs. Parrotfishes grind coral skeletons of living polyps into fine sediment with their pharyngeal teeth. A number of fishes, including many of the gorgeous butterflies, feed directly on the fleshy polyps.

Pocillopora eydouxi

Pocillopora verrucosa

Stylophora pistillata

Pocillopora damicornis

Seriatopora hystrix

Seriatopora hystrix

Palauastrea ramosa

Montipora aequituberculata

Montipora capricornis

Montipora confusa

Montipora danae

Montipora digitata

Montipora monasteriata

Montipora spumosa

Montipora stellata

Montipora sp.

Montipora sp.

Montipora sp.

Montipora sp.

Anacropora forbesi

Anacropora puertogalerae

Acropora cerealis

Acropora danai

Acropora elseyi

Acropora digitifera

Acropora echinata

Acropora florida

Acropora formosa

Acropora formosa

Acropora formosa

Acropora grandis

Acropora horrida

Acropora humilis

Acropora hyacinthus

Mixed *Acropora* corals, mainly *A. hyacinthus*

Acropora latistella

Acropora loripes

Acropora millepora

Acropora monticulosa

Acropora nasuta?

Acropora palifera

Acropora nobilis

Acropora palifera

Acropora palifera

Acropora robusta

Acropora valenciennesi

Acropora secale

Acropora subglabra

Acropora sp.

Astreopora gracilis

Porites antennuata

Porites antennuata

Porites cylindrica

Porites latistella

Porites nigrescens

Porites rus

Porites sp.

Porites sp.

Goniopora columna

Goniopora sp.

Goniopora sp.

Goniopora sp.

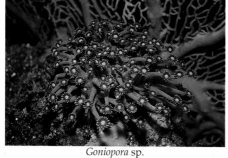

Goniopora sp.

Goniopora sp.

Alveopora catalai

Alveopora fenestrata

Alveopora spongiosa

Alveopora sp.

Psammocora contigua (Siderastreidae)

Alveopora sp. (Poritidae)

Psammocora digitata (Siderastreidae)

Coscinaraea columna (Siderastreidae)

Pavona cactus

Pavona clavus

Pavona explanulata

Pavona minuta

Leptoseris gardineri

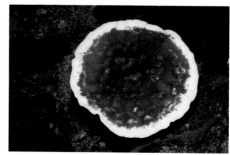

Leptoseris hawaiiensis

Leptoseris mycetoseroides

Leptoseris scabra

Gardineroseris planulata

Coeloseris mayeri

Pachyseris foliosa

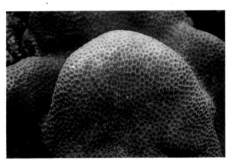

Coeloseris mayeri

Pachyseris rugosa

Pachyseris rugosa

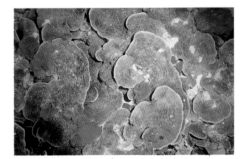

Pachyseris speciosa

Cycloseris cyclolites

Diaseris fragilis

Heliofungia actiniformis

Fungia concinna

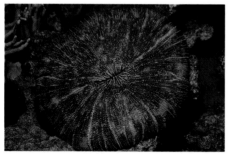

Fungia fungites

Fungia moluccensis

Fungia repanda

Fungia simplex

Fungia scutaria

Fungia valida

Ctenactis echinata

Herpolitha limax

Polyphyllia talpina

Halomitra pileus

Sandalolitha robusta

Lithophyllon sp.

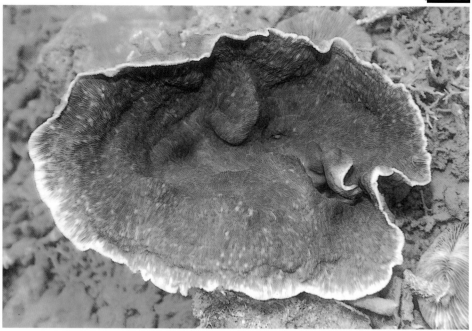

Podabacia crustacea (Fungiidae)

Zoopilus echinatus (Fungiidae)

Galaxea astreata (Oculinidae)

Galaxea fascicularis (Oculinidae)

Acrhelia horrescens (Oculinidae)

Echinophyllia orpheensis

Oxypora glabra

Oxypora lacera

Mycedium elephantotus

Pectinia alcicornis

Pectinia alcicornis

Pectinia lactuca

Pectinia paeonia

Blastomussa wellsi

Cynarina lacrymalis

Scolymia australis

Scolymia vitiensis

Lobophyllia corymbosa

Lobophyllia corymbosa

Lobophyllia diminuta

Lobophyllia hataii

Lobophyllia hemprichii

Symphyllia agaricia

Lobophyllia hemprichii

Lobophyllia robusta

Symphyllia radians

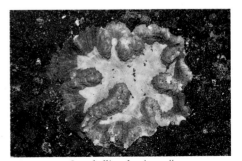

Symphyllia recta

Symphyllia valenciennesii

Merulina ampliata

Hydnophora exesa

Hydnophora grandis

Hydnophora microconos

Hydnophora rigida

Caulastrea furcata

Favia favus

Favia lizardensis

Favia matthaii

Favia pallida

Favia speciosa

Favia stelligera

Barbattoia amicorum

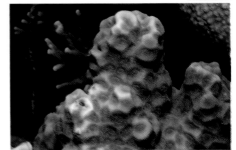

Favites abdita

Favites flexuosa

Favites complanata

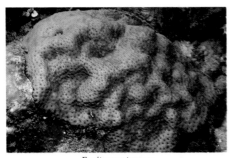

Favites pentagona

Favites sp.

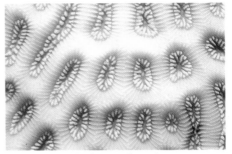

Goniastrea australensis

Goniastrea palauensis

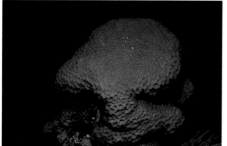

Goniastrea pectinata

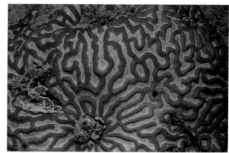

Platygyra daedalea

Platygyra lamellina

Platygyra pini

Platygyra ryukyuensis

Platygyra ryukyuensis

Platygyra sinensis

Platygyra sp.

Platygyra sp.

Leptoria phrygia

Leptoria phrygia

Oulophyllia crispa

Oulophyllia bennettae

Oulophyllia bennettae

Montastrea annuligera

Montastrea curta

Montastrea magnistellata

Diploastrea heliopora

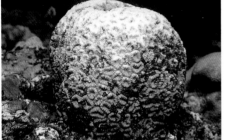

Montastrea valenciennesi

Montastrea sp.

Leptastrea inaequalis

Cyphastrea serailia

Cyphastrea microphthalma

Echinopora horrida

Echinopora pacificus

Echinopora lamellosa

Echinopora mammiformis

Echinopora pacificus

Echinopora sp.

Trachyphyllia geoffroyi (Trachyphylliidae)

Euphyllia ancora

Euphyllia divisa

Euphyllia glabrescens

Euphyllia paradivisa

Euphyllia paradivisa

Catalaphyllia jardinei

Plerogyra sinuosa

Physogyra lichtensteini

Turbinaria peltata

Turbinaria frondens

Turbinaria sp.

Turbinaria reniformis

Tubastraea faulkneri

Tubastraea sp.

Tubastraea sp.

Tubastraea micrantha

Tubastraea micrantha

Chapter 8

Soft Corals and Sea Fans
Undersea Wildflowers

Soft corals and their relatives are a prominent part of the reef scene. In some places they may form extensive growths, like vast fields of undersea wildflowers. They occur in all reef habitats, but achieve their most impressive growth forms in deeper parts of the reef, between about 10-30 meters depth. Foremost in this respect is the gorgeous multi-hued *Dendronephthya*. When fully expanded the colonies look like fluffy cotton candy, exhibiting dazzling shades of pink, red, purple, and yellow. These same depths, especially on steep outer slopes, are the domain of gorgonians, commonly known as sea fans and whips. All the above belong to the group known as Alcyonaria, a Subclass within the Phylum Cnidaria (containing jellyfish, hydrozoans, hard corals, etc.).

Structure

Structurally alcyonarians are similar to hard corals. Both contain colonies of polyps that gather planktonic food. However, as their name suggests, soft corals lack a hard limestone skeleton. Instead, the supporting "stem" consists of fleshy tissue that is reinforced by a matrix of microscopic calcareous particles (sclerites). These are sometimes similar in appearance to sponge spicules, but much more diverse in shape. The shape, size, and ornamentation (thorns, tubercles, spines, and warts) of sclerites are the most useful features used by scientists to identify species. Sea fans and sea whips have a more rigid horny skeleton

that is usually coated with a softer outer "rind". When their polyps are fully extended hard corals frequently resemble soft varieties, but they can be distinguished upon closer inspection. Soft corals have tiny pinnae (side branches) on the tentacles in contrast to the smooth tentacles of hard corals. Moreover, soft corals generally have eight tentacles (and are thus known as octocorals) compared to six tentacles or multiples of six found in hard corals (hexacorals).

A particular type of soft coral may drastically alter its appearance depending on whether its polyps are extended or retracted. In addition the central stalk and fleshy sponge-like tissue can expand, contract, or wrinkle over a considerable range. Most soft corals are various shades of green, yellow, and brown. The color is largely attributable to the presence of single celled algae that live within their tissue. This is the same algae (zooanthellae) that live in association with hard corals. They provide a very significant source of nutrition to both hard and soft corals by leaking energy rich sugars into their hosts. Some gorgonian fans and whips also contain zooxanthellae in their soft outer coating.

Potential wonder drugs

Alcyonarians are one of the few types of reef organisms that seldom have encrusting growths of algae, sponges, ascidians, etc. on their surface. The numerous feeding polyps help to prevent unwanted colonizers. Various chemical secretions also inhibit marine growths. For

◄ Luxuriant growth of *Dendronepthya*, Fiji Islands.

Soft Corals & Sea Fans

this reason soft corals and other alcyonarians (and also sponges) have been the focus of considerable medical research. It is hoped that substances may be discovered that will inhibit cancerous growths and other diseases.

Most soft corals, fans, and whips rely on the current for a continuous supply of minute food organisms. This reliance is readily apparent in sea fans and whips. They are especially abundant and reach their largest size where currents are periodically strong. In prime situations sea fans may measure three meters or more in width. They invariably project from the reef's surface at an angle that offers maximum exposure to the prevailing currents.

Sea pens

Sandy bottoms are the home of a special group (Order Pennatulacea) of cnidarians known as sea pens. The common name is derived from their resemblance to a quill pen. Colonies of polyps are situated on numerous branches that radiate from a central stalk, giving a feather-like appearance. Sea pens are most commonly seen at night, but it is not unusual to find some species out during the day.

Black and blue corals

Although they are actually more closely related to hard corals and anemones we include black corals (Order Antipatharia) in this chapter. They assume a variety of branched or whip-like growth forms that superficially resemble gorgonians. The name black coral is derived from the color of the hard inner skeleton. The live colo-

nies are never black when viewed underwater. They are usually brown, whitish, or various shades of yellow. Black corals and certain gorgonians are sometimes commercially harvested for making jewelry. They can sometimes be seen in only a few meters depth, but the best quality suitable for cutting and polishing is found in much deeper water, often below 50 meters.

Blue coral (*Heliopora*) is easily mistaken for a hard or scleractinian coral because of its brittle structure and massive size. However, microscopic examination of its polyps reveal that it is a true octocoral and therefore a close relative of soft corals and fans.

Alcyonarian Identification

Soft corals and gorgonian fans are very difficult to identify from photographs. Positive identification is largely dependent on the microscopic examination of a specimen sample. The experts we consulted were therefore hesitant in providing scientific names for some species or could only provide family names. Uncertain identifications are therefore indicated with a question mark.

Soft coral, *Scleronephthya* sp. (Nephtheidae), large colony.

Soft coral, *Alcyonium* sp., 30 cm height.

Soft coral, *Lobophyton* sp., 60 cm width.

Soft coral, *Lobophyton* sp., 60 cm width.

Soft coral, *Lobophyton* sp., 40 cm width.

Soft coral, *Lobophyton* sp., 80 cm width.

Soft coral, *Lobophyton*? sp., 100 cm width.

Soft coral, *Lobophyton* sp., 40 cm width.

Orange alcyonarian, *Minabea aldersladei*, 30 cm.

Soft coral, *Sarcophyton crassocaule,* large colony.

Soft coral, *Sarcophyton* sp., 40 cm width.

Soft coral, *Sarcophyton* sp., 70 cm width.

Soft coral, *Sarcophyton* sp., large colony.

Soft coral, *Sarcophyton* sp., 6 cm width.

Soft coral, *Sinularia* sp., 80 cm width.

Soft coral, *Sinularia* sp., 50 cm width.

Soft coral, *Sinularia* sp., 40 cm width

Soft coral, *Sinularia* sp., 40 cm width.

Soft coral, *Sinularia* sp., 120 cm width.

Soft coral, *Sinularia* sp., 120 cm width.

Soft coral, *Sinularia* sp., 50 cm width.

Soft coral *Sinularia* sp., 60 cm width.

Soft coral, *Sinularia* sp., 70 cm width.

Soft coral, *Sinularia* sp., 50 cm width.

Soft coral, *Sinularia* sp., 50 cm width.

Soft Corals

Soft coral, *Sinularia* sp. (Alcyoniidae),
40 cm width.

Soft coral, *Sinularia* sp. (Alcyoniidae),
70 cm width.

Soft coral, *Sinularia* sp. (Alcyoniidae),
80 cm width.

Soft coral, *Sinularia* sp. (Alcyoniidae),
40 cm width.

Gorgonian fan, *Echinogorgia* sp.(Plexauridae),
120 cm height.

Gorgonian fan (possibly Acanthogorgiidae),
150 cm height.

Soft coral, *Alertigorgia* sp.(Anthothelidae),
100 cm height.

Briareum soft coral, *Briareum* sp. (Briareidae),
colony width 10 cm.

Gorgonian fan, *Subergorgia mollis* (Subergorgiidae), 250 cm width.

Briareum soft coral, *Briareum* sp.(Briareidae),
large colony.

Sea fan, *Solenocaulon* sp. (Anthothelidae),
30 cm height.

Unidentified sea fan (possibly Anthothelidae),
10 cm height.

Flower soft coral, *Clavularia* sp. (Clavulariidae),
colony width 12 cm.

Organ pipe coral, *Tubipora musica*, colony width 12 cm.

Organ pipe coral, *Tubipora musica*, colony width 25 cm.

Red whip coral, *Ctenocella pectinata*
100 cm height.

Red whip coral, *Junceella* sp., 80 cm height.

Yellow whip coral, *Ellisella* sp., 70 cm height.

Red whip coral, *Ellisella* sp., 60 cm height.

Delicate sea whip, *Junceella fragilis*,
180 cm height.

Delicate sea whip, *Junceella fragilis*,
150 cm height.

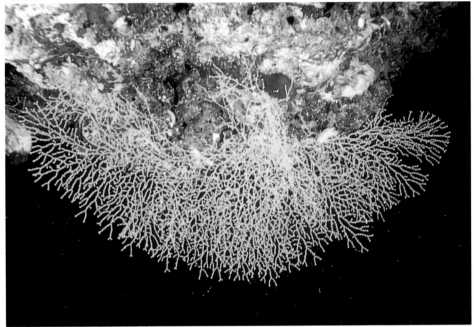

Gorgonian fan, *Acabaria* sp. (Melithaeidae), 50 cm width.

Wire coral, *Hicksonella* sp. (Gorgoniidae), 100 cm height.

Gorgonian fan, *Plumigorgia schuboti* (Ifalukellidae), 40 cm height.

Gorgonian fan, *Isis hippuris* (Isidiidae), 35 cm height.

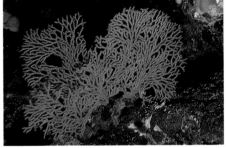

Gorgonian fan (Melithaeidae), 40 cm width.

Soft coral, *Dendronephthya* sp., 40 cm height.

Soft coral, *Dendronephthya* sp., 40 cm height.

Soft coral, *Dendronephthya* sp., 40 cm height.

Soft coral, *Dendronephthya* sp., 6 cm width.

Soft coral, *Dendronephthya* sp., 16 cm width.

Soft coral, *Dendronephthya* sp., 18 cm height.

Soft coral, *Dendronephthya* sp., 70 cm height.

Soft coral, *Dendronephthya* sp., 80 cm height.

Soft coral, *Dendronphthya* sp., 35 cm height.

Soft coral, *Lemnalia* sp., 40 cm width.

Soft coral, *Lemnalia* sp., 30 cm width.

Soft coral, *Lemnalia* sp., 40 cm width.

Soft coral, *Scleronephthya* sp. (Nephtheidae), 60 cm height.

Soft coral, *Siphonogorgia godeffroyi* (Nidaliidae), 10 cm height.

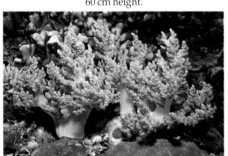

Soft coral, *Nepthea* sp. (Nephtheidae), 40 cm height.

Soft coral, *Paralemnalia* sp. (Nephtheidae), 15 cm width.

Soft coral, *Nepthea* sp. (Nephtheidae), 40 cm height.

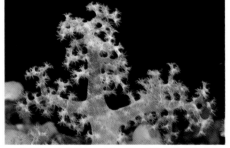

Soft coral, *Scleronephthya?* sp.(Nephtheidae), 10 cm height.

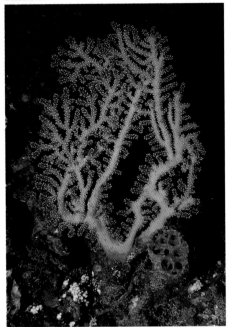

Soft coral, *Siphonogorgia* sp.
(Nidaliidae), 40 cm height.

Soft coral, *Siphonogorgia* sp.
(Nidaliidae), 10 cm height.

Soft coral, *Siphonogorgia* sp.
(Nidaliidae), 35 cm height.

Soft coral, *Siphonogorgia* sp. (Nidaliidae),
15 cm height.

Soft coral, *Siphonogorgia* sp.
(Nidaliidae), 35 cm height.

Soft coral, *Siphonogorgia* sp.
(Nidaliidae), 80 cm width.

Gorgonian fan, *Astrogorgia?* sp. (Plexauridae),
100 cm height.

Soft coral, *Echinigorgia?* sp., 30 cm height.

Soft coral, *Echinigorgia?* sp., 30 cm height.

Soft coral, *Euplexaura?* sp., 70 cm height.

Soft coral, *Echinigorgia?* sp., 40 cm height.

Soft coral, *Echinomuricea* sp., 30 cm height.

Soft coral, *Euplexaura?* sp., 150 cm height.

Sea fan, *Paracis?* sp., 30 cm height.

Soft coral (Plexauridae), 35 cm height.

Soft coral (Plexauridae), 35 cm height.

Sea fan (Plexauridae), 12 cm height.

Sea fan (Plexauridae), 120 cm.

Sea fan (Plexauridae), 150 cm height.

Flower soft coral, *Anthelia* sp. (Xeniidae),
colony width 30 cm.

Soft coral, *Efflatournaria* sp.
(Xeniidae), 30 cm height.

Flower soft coral, *Stereosoma* sp.
(Xeniidae), 30 cm width.

Flower soft coral, *Xenia* sp.
(Xeniidae), 25 cm width.

Flower soft coral, *Xenia* sp.
(Xeniidae), 60 cm height.

Flower soft coral, *Xenia* sp.
(Xeniidae), 15 cm height.

Flower soft coral, *Xenia* sp.
(Xeniidae), 15 cm height.

Unidentified sea fan, 120 cm height.

Unidentified sea fan, 30 cm height.

Unidentified sea fan, 30 cm height.

Unidentified sea fan, 40 cm height.

Unidentified sea fan, 12 cm height.

Unidentified sea fan, 12 cm height.

Unidentified sea fan, 60 cm height.

Unidentified sea fan, 15 cm height.

Sea pen, *Pteroeides* sp. (Pteroeidae), 18 cm height.

Sea pen, *Pteroeides* sp. (Pteroeidae), 10 cm height.

Sea pen, *Virgularia* sp. (Virgulariidae), 20 cm height.

Sea pen, *Virgularia* sp. (Virgulariidae), 12 cm height.

Sea pen, *Virgularia sp.*, 25 cm height.

Sea pen, *Virgularia?* sp., 10 cm height.

Sea pen, *Virgularia?* sp., 10 cm height.

Sea pen, *Virgularia?* sp., 10 cm height.

Blue coral, *Heliopora coerulea.*

Blue coral, *Heliopora coerulea.*

Black coral, *Antipathes* sp., 180 cm height.

Black coral, *Antipathes* sp., 120 cm height.

Spiral coral, *Cirrhipathes spiralis*, 100 cm length.

Black coral, *Antipathes* sp., 120 cm height.

Black coral, *Antipathes* sp., 150 cm height.

Black coral, *Antipathes* sp., 160 cm height.

Black coral, *Antipathes* sp., 120 cm height.

Black coral, *Antipathes* sp., 80 cm height.

Chapter 9

Marine Worms
An Amazing Abundance

Coral reefs are well and truly riddled with worms. A study at Heron Island on the Great Barrier Reef revealed that a single small coral head harbored 1400 individual worms belonging to 103 species! Most reef worms are very inconspicuous. They live in a variety of micro-habitats, particularly the myriad of crevices and fissures. Many species are burrowers that live either in the dead, basement portion of the reef, or under the surface on silt, sand, and rubble bottoms. Several major categories (Phyla) of worms are found on coral reefs, but only four of the commonly seen groups are treated here.

The reef is a delicately balanced ecosystem caught in a tug-of-war between constructive and destructive processes. Boring worms destroy huge quantities of living coral and their burrows form an endless labyrinth in the reef's foundation. Worms physically pulverize the coral with their horny teeth. There is also evidence that they attack it chemically by dissolving its calcium carbonate matrix.

Flatworms

Flatworms belong to the Phylum Platyhelminthes. Included in this group are the liver flukes and tapeworms. These notorious human parasites and the common flatworms (polyclads) found on coral reefs are miles apart in general appearance. At first glance polyclads can easily be mistaken for nudibranchs (see Chapter 12). They have a much flattened, oval body and exhibit dazzling color patterns.

Their bright livery probably warns predators that they are toxic or distasteful. Otherwise these exposed, slow-moving creatures would easily become victims of worm-feeding fishes. Most species are under about 8 cm in length. Their locomotion is achieved by sliding across a self-secreted mat of mucus. The actual movement is powered by numerous microscopic bristles. Flatworms can regenerate an entire new animal from a detached fragment, but can also reproduce sexually.

Polychaete worms

Segmented worms are members of the Phylum Annelida. The best known terrestrial representative is undoubtedly the earthworm. The most visible types of segmented worms found on coral reefs belong to a group known as polychaetes. They have a variety of shapes and life styles. The highly ornate and conspicuous Christmas tree and feather duster worms are common on most reefs. Young worms settle on coral heads and secrete a tube that kills the underlying polyps. New coral growth quickly surrounds the tube. Meanwhile the worm occupant secretes additional tube material to keep pace with the coral. The worm lives permanently in its tube. Only the brightly colored, feather-like feeding tentacles protrude from its lair. These are used to snare tiny planktonic organisms. These appendages are ultra sensitive to light and pressure changes. When disturbed they are quickly withdrawn into the tube.

◄ Tube worm, *Sabella* sp. (Sabellidae), 5 cm.

Sexes are usually separate in polychaete worms. Eggs and sperm are simultaneously released into the surrounding water. Fertilized eggs develop into free-swimming larvae called trochophores. These eventually settle onto the reef after a variable period, frequently of 2-3 weeks duration.

Eggs and sperm of the reef-dwelling Palolo worm (genus *Eunice*) become concentrated in the tail segment of sexually mature adults. At dawn one week after the November full moon the tails become detached and float to the surface. They then break apart resulting in fertilization. In some areas hundreds of thousands of segments are released forming a thick soup on the surface. Samoans and other Pacific islanders consider them a gastronomic delicacy and eagerly await the breeding season each year.

Ribbon worms

Ribbon worms of the Phylum Nemertea are common on coral reefs. As the name suggests they are flattened, elongate creatures. Unlike polychaetes, they are unsegmented. One of their most notable features is an extendible proboscis. Most species are very small, usually 1-3 cm, but a few reach 5-10 cm or slightly larger. Although many are brightly colored, they are generally cryptic in habit. Most reef species are found under rocks or dead coral slabs, in rocky fissures, among algae or in soft bottom sediments. They feed on other small invertebrates and their eggs.

Acorn worms

Acorn worms (Phylum Hemichordata) are inconspicuous creatures that live on sand or silt bottoms, generally in U-shaped burrows. Although the animals themselves are not usually seen by divers, they deposit very distinctive coils of sand above the burrow (see page 131).

Acoelous flatworms, Order Acoela, on soft coral, 1 cm.

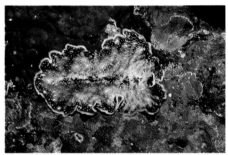

Polyclad flatworm, *Acanthozoon* sp. (Pseudoceratidae), 3 cm. (L. Newman & A. Flowers).

Polyclad flatworm, *Pseudobiceros bedfordi* (Pseudo-ceratidae), 3 cm. (L. Newman & A. Flowers).

Polyclad flatworm, *Pseudobiceros gratus* (Pseudoceratidae), 3 cm. (L. Newman & A.Flowers).

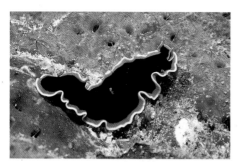

Polyclad flatworm, *Pseudobiceros hancockanus*, 3 cm. (L. Newman & A. Flowers).

Polyclad flatworm, *Pseudobiceros gloriosus* 3 cm. (L. Newman & A. Flowers).

Polyclad flatworm, *Pseudobiceros fulgcr*, 3 cm. (L. Newman & A. Flowers).

Polyclad flatworm, *Pseudoceros bifurcus*, 3 cm. (L. Newman & A. Flowers).

Polyclad flatworm, *Pseudoceros bimarginatus*, 3 cm. (L. Newman & A. Flowers).

Polyclad flatworm, *Pseudoceros dimidiatus*, 3 cm.

Polyclad flatworm, *Pseudoceros ferrugineus*, 3 cm.

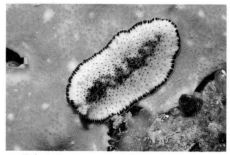

Polyclad flatworm, *Pseudoceros leptostichus*, 3 cm. (L. Newman & A. Flowers).

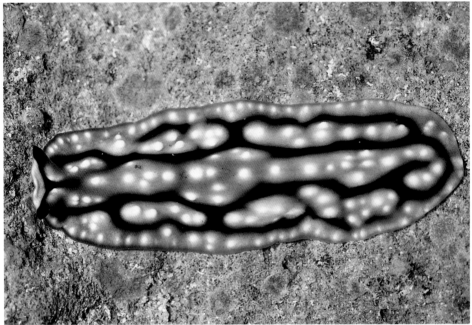

Polyclad flatworm, *Pseudoceros imitatus*, 3 cm.

Polyclad flatworm, *Pseudoceros gravieri*, 3 cm.

Polyclad flatworm, *Pseudoceros* sp.,
3 cm. (L. Newman & A. Flowers).

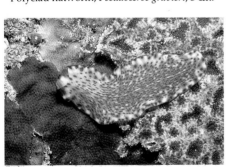

Polyclad flatworm, *Pseudoceros* sp.,
3 cm. (L. Newman & A. Flowers).

Polyclad flatworm, *Thysanozoon* sp., 3 cm.

Bristle worm, *Chloeia*? sp. (Polychaeta, Amphionidae), 8 cm.

Bristle worm, *Eurythoe complanata* (Polychaeta, Amphionidae), 10 cm.

Palolo worm, *Eunice* sp. (Polychaeta, Eunicidae), 10 cm.

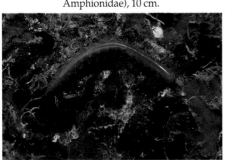

Polychaete worm, *Leocrates chinensis*? (Polychaeta, Hesionidae), 5 cm.

Polychaete worm (Polychaeta, Hesionidae), 5 cm.

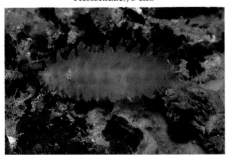

Scale worm, *Lepidonotus* sp. (Polychaeta, Polynoidae), 4 cm.

Scale worm, *Gastrolepidia clavigera* (Polychaeta, Polynoidae), 4 cm, on holothurian.

Tubeworm, *Filogranella elatensis* (Polychaeta, Serpulidae), colony height 20 cm.

Tubeworm, *Protula magnifica* (Polychaeta, Serpulidae), 6 cm.

Tubeworm, *Protula* sp. (Polychaeta, Serpulidae), 6 cm.

Christmas tree worm, *Spirobranchus giganteus* (Polychaeta, Serpulidae), 3 cm.

Christmas tree worm, *Spirobranchus giganteus* (Polychaeta, Serpulidae).

Christmas tree worm, *Spirobranchus giganteus* (Polychaeta, Serpulidae), 3 cm.

Tubeworm (Polychaeta, Sabellidae), 3 cm.

Tubeworm, *Sabellastarte* sp. (Polychaeta, Sabellidae), 6 cm.

Tubeworm (Polychaeta, Sabellidae),
10 cm diameter.

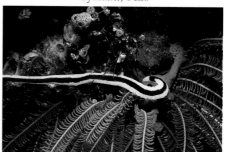

Unidentified ribbon worm (Nemertea), 8 cm.

Hydroid-eating worm (Polychaeta,
Syllidae), 4 cm.

Spaghetti worm (Polychaeta, Terebellidae),
tentacles 100 cm.

Ribbon worm, *Baseodiscus hemprichii*
(Nemertea), 80 cm.

Tubeworm , *Phoronis* sp. (Phylum Phorona), 3 cm.

Tubular deposit from Acorn worm
(Hemichordata).

Chapter 10

Crustaceans
Armored Knights of the Sea

The crustaceans are one of the truly dominant groups living on coral reefs. However, due to the tiny size and cryptic habits of many species, it is easy to grossly under-estimate their impact on the reef's ecology. The group is incredibly diverse with regards to size, shapes, colors, and life style. Not only does it include well known representatives such as lobsters, shrimps, and crabs, but also a wealth of microscopic organisms that form a large portion of both the planktonic and benthic interstitial fauna.

The Class Crustacea belongs to the Phylum Arthropoda which includes the land-dominating insects, spiders, scorpions, millipedes, and centipedes. The phylum is huge, outnumbering all other animal groups combined by a ratio of three to one. It is estimated that three quarter of a million species have been described, of which crustaceans account for only about 30,000 species.

Crustaceans are typified by the presence of a rigid, calcium carbonate-based external skeleton. Because growth is nearly continuous throughout the life cycle, the animal periodically outgrows its armor coating. Therefore the shell is shed (molted) and replaced at regular intervals. Before molting the calcium component of the shell is partly absorbed and digested, while the new shell begins to form. When the shell is finally shed and the new coat is still relatively soft the animal is particularly vulnerable to predators and therefore seeks the shelter of a burrow or other hiding place.

Crustaceans are also characterized by a segmented body, although individual segments may be hidden by the external shell. In general the body can be divided into two major sections, front and back that are referred to as the cephalothorax and abdomen. Another typical feature is the jointed limbs with internal muscular attachment, capable of movement in all directions. These serve a variety of functions that include locomotion, touch, and chemical reception, respiration, and feeding. The most conspicuous of these are the walking legs, antennae (two pair in contrast to the single pair of other arthropods), and pincer-like claws or nippers typical of crabs and shrimps.

Ten Legs

The majority of crustaceans encountered on coral reefs are known as decapods (literally meaning 10 legs). Shrimps (often called prawns), lobsters, and crabs are all prominent members of this group. For the most part they are secretive creatures that remain hidden for long periods in burrows or crevices, or under dead coral slabs. They form an integral part of the food chain, being actively hunted by larger predators, mainly fishes. They have evolved a largely inconspicuous life style in response to this pressure. Generally the best time to observe crustaceans is at night when many species emerge from their retreats to feed. There are relatively few bottom foraging predators at this time, but there is still an element of risk. For example, crab-feeding scorpionfishes (*Dendrochirus* and *Pterois*) are nocturnally active.

◀ Bumblebee shrimp, *Gnathophyllum americanum*, 1 cm.

The reef doctors

The most conspicuous crustaceans during daylight hours are those that clean parasites from fishes or that form symbiotic associations with anemones and other invertebrates. The so-called "cleaner shrimps" are frequently bright colored and may occur in large numbers. They occupy permanent "stations" that are regularly patronized by a variety of fishes. Moray eels, large groupers, and triggerfishes are among the favorite customers. The fishes assume a hovering, stationary position at the station which is a signal for one or more shrimp to climb aboard and begin their inspection. The shrimps fearlessly enter the mouth and gill cavity. They remove small parasites and also feed on the mucous coat of the fish.

Symbiosis

Shrimps and crabs form symbiotic associations with a large variety of plants and invertebrates, including sponges, anemones, corals, alcyonarians, molluscs, starfish, feather stars, holothurians, and sea urchins. The basis of the association is variable depending on the partners involved. Shrimps and crabs that live amongst the stinging tentacles of sea anemones obviously receive shelter from predatory fishes. The Boxer crab (*Lybia tesselata*) and Anemone Hermit crab (*Dardanus deformis*) carry this stategy one step further by attaching sea anemones to their claws or shell. Crustaceans that live on or within sponges may feed on trapped food particles and may benefit their host by helping to keep the water circulation system free of debris.

A very common, nonetheless interesting symbiosis exists between alpheid shrimps and small gobiid fishes. The shrimp excavates and continuously maintains the burrow, apparently receiving protection from its "watchdog" fish neighbor. The goby stands guard at the entrance

Alpheus randalli (Alpheidae), 3.5 cm, with goby.

of the burrow, signaling the shrimp with a flick of its tail, when it is safe to emerge. Experiments indicate that alpheid shrimps have extremely poor vision.

Crabs

Crabs can conveniently be assigned to two main groups, the anomurans and brachyurans. The anomurans are distinguished by a clearly evident tail section. Prominent amongst this group are the well known hermit crabs (family Paguridae). Unlike most crabs that hide themselves during the molting process, the hermit does not suffer these periods of high vulnerability. Instead it simply finds a new, larger shell to accommodate its increased body size.

There are several other prominent anomuran families occurring on coral reefs. The so-called squat lobsters (actually crabs, family Galatheidae), have a curious pointed beak and are frequently associated with feather stars. Porcelain crabs (family Porcellanidae) are commonly found living among coral or may also be commensal with various sponges and echinoderms. Ghost nippers (family Callianassidae), although seldom seen, construct conspicuous sand volcanoes up to 30-40 cm in height.

The brachyurans or true crabs lack an obvious tail section. They are very abundant on coral reefs and adjacent habitats. The most diverse and numerically abundant family in reef habitats is the Xanthidae or dark-fingered crabs. As the common name suggests many of the species have dark or dark-tipped claws. Another large group includes the swimming crabs (family Portunidae). This family, which contains the well known edible mud or mangrove crab (*Scylla serrata*) is characterized by having the hindmost (fifth) pair of legs strongly flattened, an adaptation for both swimming and burrowing. Shore crabs

(family Grapsidae) are readily recognized by their broad-fronted, square-backed shape and often have a flattened appearance. They are common in the intertidal zone of rocky shores. Ghost and fiddler crabs (family Ocypodidae) are frequently seen on sandy beaches or on mud flats. They are readily distinguished by large erect eye stalks. Ghost crabs are primarily nocturnal and excavate burrows marked by piles of sand along the beach.

Sexes are always separate in decapods. They frequently exhibit elaborate courtship behavior. Internal fertilization occurs when the abdomens of the mating pair are in close proximity. Eggs are generally carried by the female on the underside of the abdominal section. After hatching the young larvae pass through a series of progressively developed stages, eventually settling on the reef and assuming the adult form.

Non-decapods

The remaining crustacean groups are generally classified as non-decapods. Barnacles were once thought to belong to a separate group, but detailed studies of their life history and anatomy reveal they are modified crustaceans. They have a typical free-swimming crustacean larval stage known as a nauplius. The larva eventually settles onto a suitable substratum and attaches by secreting a glue-like substance. At this stage it takes on the appearance of an adult, characterized by an external shell (actually a series of plates) and internal adductor muscles. The typical jointed appendages are modified to form feeding cirri. These structures are extended outside the shell and their beating movements create a current that conveys planktonic food organisms to the mouth. There are three main types of barnacles. Stalked or gooseneck barnacles are often attached to floating logs or other debris. They are easily identified on the basis of the leathery stalk that attaches the shell to the substratum. Acorn barnacles resemble miniature volcanoes and are commonly attached to rocks of the intertidal zone. They also fasten to roots of mangrove trees or on the surface of whales and turtles. The final group, parasitic barnacles, are far less conspicuous. Some species bore into shells or corals, while others are vestigial sac-like organisms attached to the abdomen of crabs and other crustaceans.

Other non-decapods are primarily very small, often microscopic organisms. They occur in huge numbers among the drifting plankton, on seaweed, in coral crevices, and in the interstices of rubble and sand. Included among this group are copepods, ostracods, mysids, isopods, and amphipods. Although we have not illustrated most of these animals due to their inconspicuous nature, we cannot over emphasize their importance in the overall ecology of coral reefs. They are an integral cog in the food chain, feeding on diatoms and other single-celled plants. In turn they form the main food for many invertebrates and a host of juvenile fishes.

Isopods display the greatest morphological diversity of any crustacean group. They are well represented both on land (eg. pillbugs and slaters) and in the marine environment. The parasitic fish lice (family Cymothoidae) are perhaps the most visible types seen on coral reefs. These flattened, segmented creatures, up to about 3-4 cm in length, are often seen attached just behind the head of damselfishes and other species.

Perhaps the most conspicuous non-decapod inhabitants of coral reefs are the mantis shrimps (subclass Stomatopoda). These large (up to 30 cm), colorful, segmented creatures are sometimes seen shuffling across the bottom or suddenly retreating into their burrows. They are voracious predators of other crustaceans and small fishes, as well as molluscs and worms. Their powerful claws are used to smash the shell of their victims.

Gooseneck barnacle, *Lepas testudinata*, 5 cm (C. Bryce).

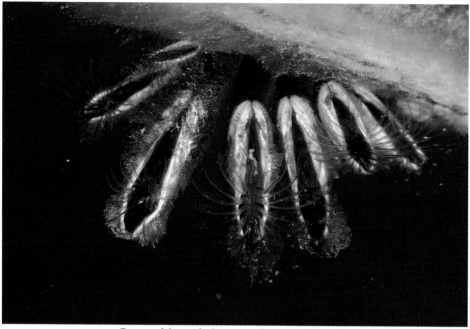

Gooseneck barnacle, *Lepas anserifera*, 3 cm (C. Bryce).

Acorn barnacle, *Tetraclita porosa*,
3 cm (C. Bryce).

Tidepool barnacle, *Tetraclita multicostata*,
2 cm (C. Bryce)

Coral barnacle, Family Pyrgomatidae,
2 cm (C. Bryce).

Fish lice, Family Cymathoidae (Isopoda), 2 cm.

Skeleton shrimp, *Caprella* sp. (Amphipoda), 2 cm.

Mantis shrimp, *Odontodactylus scyllarus* (Squillidae), 12 cm.

Mantis shrimp, *Lysiosquilla* sp. (Squillidae), 6 cm.

Mantis shrimp (Squillidae), 6 cm.

Mantis shrimp (Squillidae), 4 cm.

Mantis shrimp (Squillidae), 3 cm.

Alpheus djiboutensis, (Alpheidae), 3 cm, with goby.

Alpheus sp., (Alpheidae), 3 cm, with goby.

Alpheus sp. (Alpheidae), 3 cm.

Alpheus sp. (Alpheidae), 3 cm.

Nennalpheus sp.(Alpheidae), 2 cm.

Alpheus yaldwyni (Alpheidae), 2 cm.

Alpheus sp. (Alpheidae), 2 cm.

Axiopsis sp. (Axiidae), 2 cm.

Crinoid shrimp, *Synalpheus stimpsoni* (Hippolytidae), 2 cm.

Harlequin shrimp, *Hymenocera picta* (Gnathophyllidae), 5 cm.

Cleaner shrimp, *Lysmata amboinensis*, 4 cm.

Cleaner shrimp, *Lysmata debelius* , 5 cm.

Alpheopsis? sp., (Alpheidae) 2 cm.

Cleaner shrimp, *Lysmata multicissa?* sp., 4 cm.

Parhippolyte uveae, 5 cm.

Saron inermis , 4 cm.

Saron neglectus?, 4 cm.

Saron rectirostris, 4 cm.

Saron sp., 6 cm.

Saron sp., 10 cm.

Anemone shrimp, *Thor amboinensis*, 2 cm.

Gorgonian shrimp, *Tozeuma armatum*, 6 cm.

Reef lobster, *Enoplometopus daumi* (Nephropidae), 10 cm.

Reef lobster, *Enoplometopus debelius*
(Nephropidae), 7 cm.

Reef lobster, *Enoplometopus holthuisi*
(Nephropidae), 12 cm.

Reef lobster, *Enoplometopus occidentalis*
(Nephropidae), 10 cm.

Red-band Slipper Lobster, *Arctides regalis*
(Scyllaridae), 13 cm.

Cleaner shrimp, *Urocardidella antonbruunii,* 3 cm.

Coral shrimp, *Dasycaris zanzibarica,* 1 cm.

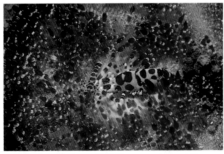

Crinoid shrimp, *Periclimenes amboinensis ,* 2 cm.

Anemone shrimp, *Periclimenes brevicarpalis,* 4 cm.

Anemone shrimp, *Periclimenes colemani,* 2 cm.

Anemone shrimp, *Periclimenes holthuisi,* 3 cm.

Anemone shrimp, *Periclimenes kororensis,* 4 cm.

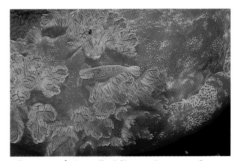

Emperor shrimp, *Periclimenes imperator,* 2 cm.

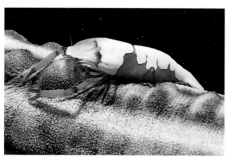

Emperor shrimp, *Periclimenes imperator*, 3 cm.

Black coral shrimp, *Periclimenes psamathe*, 3 cm.

Starfish shrimp, *Periclimenes soror*, 1 cm.

Anemone shrimp, *Periclimenes magnificus*. 6 cm.

Coral shrimp, *Vir philippinensis*, 2 cm.

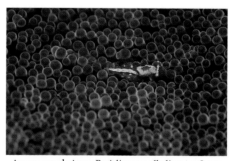

Anemone shrimp, *Periclimenes albolineatus* 2 cm.

Anemone shrimp, *Pliopontonia furtiva*, 2 cm.

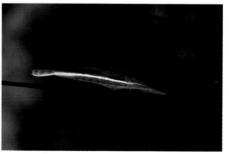

Needle shrimp, *Stegopontonia commensalis* , 2 cm.

Hingebeak shrimp, *Rhynchocinetes durbanensis*,
(Rhynchocinetidae), 3 cm.

Palaemonid shrimp, *Brachycarpus?* sp.
(Palaemonidae), 5 cm.

Hingebeak shrimp, *Rhynchocinetes hiatti*
(Rhynchocinetidae), 6 cm.

Hingebeak shrimp, *Rhynchocinetes* sp.
(Rhynchocinetidae), 6 cm.

Hingebeak shrimp, *Rhynchocinetes* sp.
(Rhynchocinetidae), 6 cm.

Cleaner shrimp, *Stenopus hispidus* (Stenopodidae), 5 cm.

Cleaner shrimp, *Stenopus pyrsonotus*
(Stenopodidae), 5 cm.

Cleaner shrimp, *Stenopus zanzibaricus*
(Stenopodidae), 4 cm.

Blue-spot rock lobster, *Panulirus femoristriga*, 40 cm.

Double-spined rock lobster,
Panulirus pencillatus, 40 cm.

Painted rock lobster, *Panulirus versicolor*, 35 cm.

Reef lobster, *Palinurella wieneckii*, 6 cm.

Slipper lobster, *Parribacus caledonicus*
(Scyllaridae), 28 cm.

Coconut crab, *Birgus latro*, 35 cm.

Land hermit crab, *Coenobita perlatus*, 10 cm.

Hermit crab, *Aniculus maximum* (Diogenidae), 10 cm.

Hermit crab, *Clibanarius seurati* (Diogenidae), 4 cm.

Hermit crab, *Dardanus guttatus* (Diogenidae), 8 cm.

Hermit crab, *Dardanus lagopodes* (Diogenidae), 7 cm.

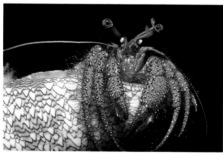

Hermit crab, *Dardanus megistos* (Diogenidae), 10 cm.

Anemone hermit crab, *Dardanus pedunculatus* (Diogenidae), 10 cm.

Hermit crab, *Trizopagrus strigatus* (Diogenidae), 8 cm.

Coral hermit crab, *Paguritta* sp. (Paguridae), 1 cm.

Elegant squat lobster, *Allogalathea elegans* (Galatheidae), 1 cm.

Pink squat lobster, *Lauriea* sp. (Galatheidae), 1 cm.

Squat lobster *Petrolisthes* sp. (Porcellanidae), 2 cm.

Squat lobster *Petrolisthes* sp. (Galatheidae), 1 cm.

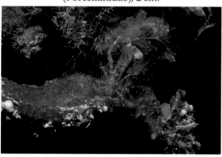

Squat lobster *Galathea* sp. (Galatheidae), 2 cm.

Porcelain crab, *Neopetrolisthes* sp. (Porcellanidae), 3 cm.

Anemone crab, *Neopetrolisthes ohshimai* (Porcellanidae), 2 cm.

Anemone crab, *Neopetrolisthes maculatus* (Porcellanidae), 4 cm.

Shore crab, *Grapsus albolineatus* (Grapsidae), 10 cm.

Shore crab, *Percnon plannissimum* (Grapsidae), 8 cm.

Shore crab, *Percnon guinotae* (Grapsidae), 10 cm.

Shore crab, *Plagusia dentipes*? (Grapsidae), 10 cm.

Sargassum crab, *Plagusia depressa tuberculata* (Grapsidae), 4 cm.

Sargassum crab, *Varuna litterata* (Grapsidae), 10 cm.

Shore crab *Plagusia dentipes* (Grapsidae), 10 cm.

Pebble crab (Leucosiidae?), 3 cm.

Box crab, *Calappa calappa*? (Calappidae), 12 cm.

Box crab, *Calappa calappa*? (Calappidae), 12 cm.

Box crab, *Calappa hepatica* (Calappidae), 5 cm.

Sponge crab, *Dromidiopsis edwardsi* (Dromiidae), 12 cm.

Sponge crab, *Sphaerodromia kendalli?* (Dromiidae), 2 cm.

Sponge crab, *Petalomera* sp. (Dromiidae), 3 cm.

Urchin crab, *Zebrida adamsii* (Eumedonidae), 1 cm.

Red land crab, *Gecarcoidea natalis* (Gecarinidae), 12 cm (Christmas Island, Indian Ocean only).

Decorator crab, *Camposcia retusa* (Majidae), 6 cm.

Decorator crab, *Camposcia retusa* (Majidae), 5 cm.

Dendronephthya crab, *Hoplophrys oatesii* (Majidae), 0.5 cm.

Spider crab, *Chirostylus* sp. (Chirostylidae), 5 cm.

Algae crab, *Huenia* sp. (Majidae), 3 cm (C. Bryce).

Ornamental crab, *Schizophrys dama* (Majidae), 3 cm.

Ornamental crab, *Schizophrys dama* (Majidae), 2 cm.

Black coral crab, *Xenocarcinus conicus* (Majidae), 2 cm.

Arrowhead crab *Huenia heraldica*, 2 cm.

Red spider crab *Menaethius orientalis*, 2 cm.

Soft coral crab, *Naxioides taurus*, 2 cm.

Spider crab *Acheus ? japonicus*, 2 cm.

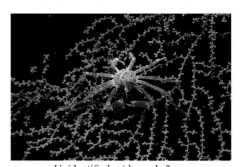

Unidentified spider crab, 3 cm.

Spider crab *Oncinopus* sp., 4 cm.

Spider crab *Schizophrys aspera*, 6 cm.

Soldier crab, *Mictyris* sp., 2 cm.

Ghost crab, *Ocypode cerathopthalma*, 10 cm.

Pea crab, *Xanthasia murigera* (Pinnotheridae), 2 cm.

Swimmer crab, *Lissocarcinus laevis* (Portunidae), 3 cm.

Spider crab, *Cyclocoeloma tuberculata* (Majidae), 3 cm.

Swimmer crab, *Portunus* sp. (Portunidae), 2 cm.

Sargassum crab, *Portunus* sp. (Portunidae), 2 cm.

Swimmer crab, *Thalamita ? prymna* (Portunidae), 12 cm.

Swimmer crab, *Charybdis* sp. (Portunidae), 6 cm.

Swimmer crab, *Portunus* sp. (Portunidae), 1 cm.

Swimmer crab, *Carupa tenuipes* (Portunidae), 2 cm

Swimmer crab, *Caphyra* sp. (Portunidae), 2 cm.

Swimmer crab, *Charybdis* sp. (Portunidae), 3 cm.

Spanner crab, *Ranina ranina* (Raninidae), 12 cm.

Spanner crab, *Raninoides serratifrons?* (Raninidae), 3 cm.

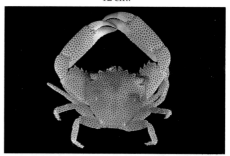

Trapezia crab, *Trapezia rufopunctata* (Trapeiziidae), 3 cm (C. Bryce).

Gorgonian crab, *Quadrella granulosa* (Trapeziidae), 2 cm. (OMIT)

Black coral crab, *Quadrella maculosa* (Trapeziidae), 10 cm.

Reef crab, *Etisus splendidus*, 15 cm.

Reef crab, *Carpilius maculatus*, 10 cm.

Reef crab, *Atergatis floridus*, 7 cm.

Reef crab, *Atergatis floridus*. 8 cm.

Reef crab, *Liomera rubra*, 2 cm.

Red-eyed crab, *Eriphia sebana*
(Menippidae), 8 cm.

Reef crab, *Atergatopsis germanini*
(Xanthidae), 8 cm.

Hairy crab, *Pilumnus verspertillo*
(Pilumnidae), 4 cm.

Reef crab, *Pseudoliomera speciosa*
(Xanthidae), 2 cm.

Reef crab, *Liomera ? laevis*
(Xanthidae), 2 cm.

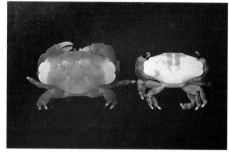

Reef crab, *Liomera cinctimana*
(Xanthidae), 2 cm.

Reef crab, *Etisus bifrontalis*
(Xanthidae), 2 cm.

Reef crab, *Paraetisus* sp.
(Xanthidae), 2 cm.

Reef crab, *Carpilius convexus* (Xanthidae), 8 cm.

Reef crab, *Zosimus aeneus* (Xanthidae), 4 cm.

Reef crab, *Tweedieia odhneri* (Xanthidae), 2 cm.

Reef crab, *Carpilius convexus* form, 10 cm

Hawiian boxer crab,Lybia edmondsoni, 3 cm.

Chapter 11

Sea Shells
Incredible Diversity

Sea shells and their relatives comprise one of the largest divisions of the animal kingdom with a species total in excess of 100,000. It is not surprising that a group of this size exhibits amazing diversity. There seems very little in common between a microscopic, shelled gastropod and a 20-metre long squid, but both belong to the Phylum Mollusca. There are actually three major types (Classes) of molluscs occurring on coral reefs. Two of these, the gastropods and bivalves are treated in this chapter. Although the colorful nudibranchs and their close relatives actually belong to the gastropod group they are covered separately in Chapter 12. Likewise, the third major group, the cephalopods are featured in Chapter 13.

It is difficult to formulate a simple definition of a group so large and diverse as molluscs. Most types possess a shell of calcium carbonate that is secreted throughout the lifespan. However, many molluscs, including snails, nudibranchs, and some cephalopods have lost their shells entirely or it is much reduced. Another common feature is the radula, specialized horny teeth used for feeding and capturing prey. In the cone shells this structure is modified to form a single, harpoon-like tooth. A well-developed set of gills used for respiration is another characteristic of most marine molluscs.

The two main divisions of shells are easily identified. Gastropods have a single solid shell, that is frequently coiled in some fashion. Bivalves, just as the name implies, have two parts to their shell.

Gastropods

Gastropods are by far the most common type of shell encountered on coral reefs. They are keenly sought by shell collectors (see accompanying box). In spite of their abundance gastropods are not always conspicuous. Extensive beds of live coral harbor relatively few species. The best mollusc areas are in places dominated by rubble, dead coral slabs, and boulders. They are also common on sandy bottoms, although here they are usually buried. Weed beds are also fertile collecting grounds, particularly for a variety of tiny species collectively known as micromolluscs.

Most of the body of a typical gastropod is hidden within its shell, which offers protection from predators. However, the smaller species are not immune to the powerful crushing teeth of triggerfishes and some wrasses. Aside from the shell, the only other body part usually seen is the muscular foot. This organ is extended and provides a slow, but steady form of crawling-type locomotion. The foot also secretes mucus which cuts down friction. When disturbed the foot is completely retracted and in some shells there is a solid "trapdoor", a membranous sheath (operculum) that seals the aperture. The inner surface of the shell is lined by an organ called the mantle. Special cells in this structure secrete the calcium carbonate matrix of the shell. In cowries and their relatives the mantle can often be seen temporarily enveloping the outer surface and is responsible for maintaining the shell's brilliant lustre.

◄ Leaf oyster, *Lopha folium* (Ostreidae), 12 cm, covered with red sponge.

The feeding habits of gastropods are just as variable as their external appearance. The handsome Triton trumpet is one of the few known predators of the notorious Crown-of-thorns starfish, which in turn feeds on live corals. It was once feared that a reduction in Trumpet shell abundance due to shell collectors was a contributing factor in starfish population explosions on the Great Barrier Reef. However, the Trumpet's role in keeping starfish populations in check appears to be over exaggerated. Recent data indicates that natural population numbers of the Trumpet are far too small to be a significant controlling factor. In some areas of Western Australia significant damage to reefs has been attributed to coral-feeding *Drupa* shells. It's hard to believe that a tiny 3-cm shell could pose such a threat. Unfortunately they multiply rapidly, sometimes reaching plague proportions. The feeding habits of some of the most commonly seen gastropods are summarized in the accompanying box.

Bivalves

Bivalves are usually burrowers or are attached to the bottom. Clams, oysters, and mussels are common examples familiar to most of us. Because they are unable to actively search for food, most rely on their elaborate gill structure to filter out tiny plants and animals. Water is pumped into the mantle cavity through an incurrent siphon and pumped out via a separate excurrent siphon. The Giant clam (*Tridachna gigas*) is perhaps the best known bivalve encountered on coral reefs. Reaching a diameter of 1.5 meters, it is reputed to live up to 200 years. This species and other members of the genus possess zooxanthellae, microscopic algal cells, in their exposed mantles. The alga actually produces food for its host, and apparently very little extra nutrients are required. The mantle also contains light and pressure sensitive spots that cause the shell to quickly close its valves if disturbed. Despite sea-farers tales of men being accidentally caught in the trap-like valves it is unlikely that this could happen.

The sex is separate in most molluscs, and depending on the species, fertilization is either external or internal. Bivalves release clouds of eggs and sperm into open water. In the Giant clam both male and female organs are present in the same individual, but usually the eggs and sperm are not expelled simultaneously. The spawning of these ponderous creatures is an incredible sight. The erupting cloud of gonadal products is an underwater version of Old Faithful geyser. Somehow, perhaps by sensing changes in temperature or salinity, the spawning of the entire population of a local area is synchronized. The fertilized eggs, as in most marine gastropods and bivalves, hatch out as veliger larvae. They swim or drift in the sea for a period ranging from about 2-40 days, before finally settling on the bottom.

Chitons and aplacophorans

Chitons are a separate class (Polyplacophora), distinct from gastropods and bivalves. They are very primitive, algal-feeding molluscs distinguished by eight separate shell-plates encircled by a fleshy mantle. Only a few species are encountered on coral reefs. They are usually seen clinging tightly to boulders in shallow water or on rocky surfaces in the intertidal zone.

Aplacophorans (Class Aplacophora) , sometimes referred to as solenogasters, are primitive worm-like molluscs, mainly restricted to depths below 20 meters. However, several inhabit shallow reefs and some very tiny species form part of the interstitial fauna that lives between grains of sand. The typical mollusc shell is absent in these animals, but they do possess scattered calcareous spicules in the skin. Most species are very small, but *Epimenia verrucosa* may reach a length of 35 cm. These animals live underneath dead coral slabs.

Common gastropods....
Where do they live and what do they eat?

Limpets (Fissurellidae, Patellidae, and Achmacidae) - Mainly clinging to rocks of the intertidal zone. Algal feeders. (see page 173)

Top Shells & Turban shells (Trochidae and Turbinidae) - Occur on shallow reefs. Algal and detritus feeders. (see page 173).

Nerites (Neritidae) - Mainly the intertidal zone. Algal feeders (see page 173.)

Periwinkles (Littorinidae) - Mainly the spray zone above the high tide line. Algal feeders (see page 173).

Creepers (Cerithiidae) - On sand bottoms or just under the sand in shallow water. Algal and detritus feeders (see page 173).

Wentletraps (Epitoniidae) - Often in shallow sandy areas. Anemone feeders (see page 173).

Strombs and Scorpion Shells (Strombidae) - Shallow coral reefs in sand patches and beachrock. Algal feeders. (see page 175)

Moon shells (Naticidae) - Intertidal sandflats. Feeds on other molluscs by boring into their shells. (see page 177)

Cowries (Cypraeidae) - Under rocks and in reef crevices in a variety of depths. Feeds on algae, sponges, and detritus. (see pages 177 - 179)

Helmet shells (Cassidae) - Sandy areas below about 5 meters depth. Feeds on starfish, sea urchins, and sand dollars. (see page 169)

Trumpet shells & Frog shells (Cymatiidae and Bursidae) - In shallow water under rocks or coral slabs. Feeds on echinoderms, molluscs, tube worms, and sea squirts. (see page 181)

Murex shells (Muricidae) - Intertidal rocks, coral rubble, under piers, and on shallow reefs. Feeds on molluscs and barnacles.(see page 181)

Coral shells (Coralliophillidae) - Live on or embedded in coral. Feed on coral tissue. (see page 181)

Dog whelks (Nassariidae) - Sand and muddy bottoms. General scavengers that also feed on dead animals. (see page 183)

Olive shells (Olividae) - Nocturnally active in shallow sandy areas. Feed on a variety of molluscs and are also scavengers. (see page 183)

Mitre shells (Mitridae) - In shallow water under sand or rocks. Feeds on other molluscs. (see page 183)

Volutes (Volutidae) - Nocturnally active on sandy bottoms. Feeds on other molluscs and are scavengers. (see page 169)

Augers (Terebridae) - Buried on clean sandy bottoms. Feeds on small invertebrates. (see page 183)

Cone shells (Conidae) - Nocturnally active. Found on sandy bottoms, or under rocks and boulders. Feed on worms, molluscs and fishes. (see pages 185 - 189)

Shell Collecting

Shell collecting is a rewarding hobby for all ages. There are thousands of enthusiasts worldwide. Amateur collectors have made many worthwhile contributions to our knowledge of mollusc distribution and have even discovered previously unknown species. Very little equipment is required, only a bucket, small jars or vials to protect delicate specimens, and a sturdy knife for prying shells off rocks. Always check to make sure that collecting is permitted in the area you intend to visit. Shells occur everywhere on the coral reef and surrounding environments. Among the most productive sites are sandy bottoms (look for trails), rubble, and particularly on the underside of rocks or dead coral slabs. Remember to return slabs and rocks to their original position. Failure to do this will result in the unnecessary death of numerous encrusting animals. Always practice conservation by limiting the number of live shells taken. One or two specimens of a particular shell is plenty. Take the time to carefully inspect the shells while collecting. Immature shells, females with eggs, and any shells with scars, holes, or other imperfections should be rejected. Beach collecting of dead shells is a different story and no limits need be imposed. Immediate cleaning of live shells is essential and there are a number of recommended techniques including freezing, boiling, burying in sand, or soaking in fresh water. The sand method (with aperture directed downward) is recommended for high gloss shells such as cowries. The intent of all methods is to remove the animal tissue. A strong jet of water or piece of stout wire will aid the process in conjunction with the other techniques. Shell cleaning can be a very smelly business so remember to do it well away from any living quarters. Encrusting growths on the surface can be removed by soaking the shell in weak bleach for 1-2 days and then scrubbing with a toothbrush.

Aplacophoran, *Epimenia verrucosa* (Neomeniomorpha), 6 cm.

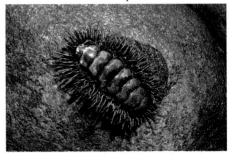

Spiny chiton, *Acanthopleura spinosa* (Chitonidae), 10 cm (C. Byrce).

Turbo, *Turbo petholatus* (Turbinidae), 5 cm.

Vermetid snail, *Serpulorbis* sp. (Vermetidae), 2 cm.

Egg cowrie, *Ovula ovum* (Ovulidae), 7 cm.

Spindle cowrie, *Phena covolva* (Ovulidae), 4 cm.

Helmut shell, *Cassis cornuta* (Cassidae), 30 cm.

Partridge tun, *Tonna perdix* (Tonnidae), 40 cm.

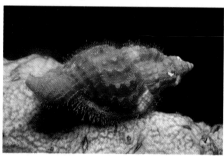

Hairy trumpet, *Cymatium lotorium* (Ranellidae), 6 cm.

Striped dog whelk, *Nassarius glans* (Nassariidae), 5 cm.

Baler shell, *Melo amphora* (Volutidae), 30 cm.

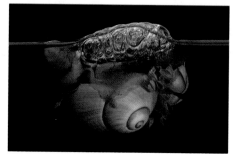

Violet snail, *Janthina janthina* (Janthinidae), 3 cm.
(C. Byrce)

Thorny oyster, *Spondylus varius* (Spondylidae), 15 cm.

Flame file shell, *Lima* sp. (Limidae), 5 cm.

Thorny oyster, *Spondylus nicobaricus?* (Spondylidae), 12 cm.

Rock oyster, *Saccostrea cuccullata* (Ostreidae), 5 cm, and various gastropod molluscs of the intertidal zone.

Coral clam, *Pedum spondyloidum* (Pectinidae), 5 cm.

Giant clam, *Tridacna gigas*, 40 cm.

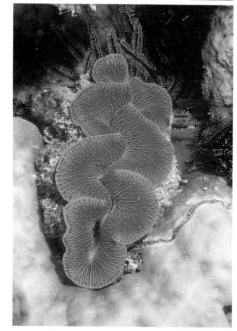

Giant clam, *Tridacna maxima*, 30 cm.

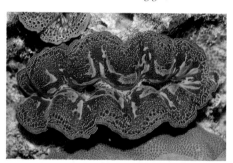

Giant clam, *Tridacna crocea* 15 cm.

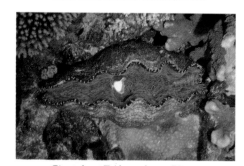

Giant clam, *Tridacna derasa*, 50 cm.

Giant clam, *Tridacna squamosa*, 30 cm.

Hippopus clam, *Hippopus hippopus*, 40 cm
(C. Bryce).

171

1. Abalone
    Haliotis asinina (Haliotidae)

2. Limpet
    Patelloida saccharina (dorsal view)
    (Acmaeidae)

3. *Patelloida saccharina* (ventral view)

4. Top shell
    Trochus maculatus (Trochidae)

5. *Trochus maculatus* (variety)

6. Limpet
    Collisella striata (dorsal view)
    (Acmaeidae)

7. *Collisella striata* (ventral view)

8. Top shell
    Tectus niloticus (Trochidae)

9. Turban shell
    Turbo petholatus (Turbinidae)

10. Turban shell
    Turbo chrysostoma (Turbinidae)

11. Periwinkle
    Tectarius pagodus (Littorinidae)

12. Periwinkle
    Littoraria scabra (Littorinidae)

13. Nerite
    Nerita plicata (Neritidae)

14. Sundial shell
    Architectonica perspectiva
    (Architectonicidae)

15. Nerite
    Nerita polita (Neritidae)

16. Wentletrap
    Epitonium scalare (Epitoniidae)

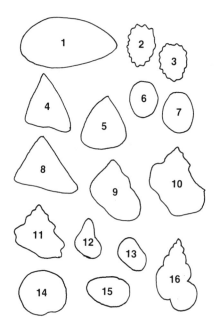

Miscellaneous Gastropods

Ass's ear abalone, *Haliotis asinina*
(Haliotidae), 10 cm.

Common turban shell, *Tectus niloticus*
(Trochidae), 12 cm.

1. Spider shell, *Lambis chiragra* (Strombidae)

2. Spider shell, *Lambis crocata* (Strombidae)

3. Stromb, *Strombus epidromis* (Strombidae)

4. Stromb, *Strombus aurisdianae* (Strombidae)

5. Stromb, *Strombus canarium* (Strombidae)

6. Spider shell, *Lambis millepeda* (Strombidae)

7. Stromb, *Strombus sinuatus* (Strombidae)

8. Stromb, *Strombus luhuanus* (Strombidae)

9. Stromb, *Strombus bulla* (Strombidae)

10. Vase shell, *Vasum ceramicum* (Vasidae)

11. Spider shell, *Lambis scorpius* (Strombidae)

12. Stromb, *Strombus lentiginosus* (Strombidae)

13. Spider shell, *Lambis lambis* (Strombidae)

14. Harp shell, *Harpa articularis* (Harpidae)

15. Harp shell, *Harpa amouretta* (Harpidae)

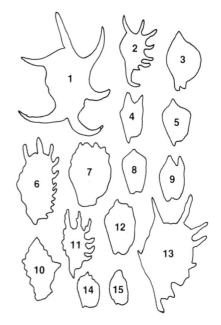

Strombs, Vase Shells, and Harp Shells

Stromb, *Strombus bulla* (Strombidae), 6 cm.

Scorpion shell, *Lambis scorpius* (Strombidae), 10 cm.

1. Moon shell, *Polinices pyriformis* (Naticidae)

2. Moon shell, *Polinices aurantius* (Naticidae)

3. *Cypraea tigris*

4. *Cypraea mauritiana*

5. *Cypraea argus*

6. *Cypraea mappa*

7. *Cypraea eglantina*

8. *Cypraea aurantium*

9. *Cypraea arabica* (dorsal view)

10. *Cypraea arabica* (ventral view)

11. *Cypraea talpa*

12. *Cypraea histrio* (dorsal view)

13. *Cypraea histrio* (ventral view)

14. *Cypraea vitellus*

15. *Cypraea testudinaria*

16. *Cypraea maculifera* (dorsal view)

17. *Cypraea maculifera* (ventral view)

18. *Cypraea carneola* (dorsal view)

19. *Cypraea carneola* (ventral view)

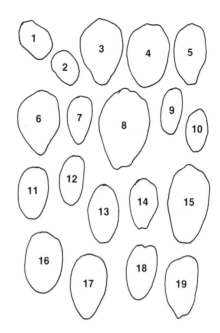

Cowries-Cypraeidae, etc.

Valentia cowry, *Cypraea valentia*, 7 cm.

Cribraria cowry, *Cypraea cribraria*, 3 cm.

1. *Cypraea lynx*

2. *Cypraea onyx*

3. *Cypraea caputserpentis*

4. *Cypraea miliaris*

5. *Cypraea teres*

6. *Cypraea helvola*

7. *Cypraea felina*

8. *Cypraea annulus*

9. *Cypraea moneta*

10. *Cypraea limacina*

11. *Cypraea cribraria*

12. *Cypraea labrolineata*

13. *Cypraea isabella*

14. *Cypraea errones*

15. *Cypraea asellus*

16. *Cypraea staphylaea*

17. *Cypraea ovum*

18. *Cypraea erosa*

19. *Cypraea chinensis*

20. *Cypraea nucleus*

21. *Cypraea caurica*

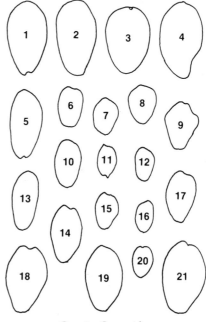

Cowries-Cypraeidae

Onyx cowry, *Cypraea onyx*, 3 cm.

Tiger cowry, *Cypraea tigris*, 8 cm.

1. Helmet shell, *Casmaria erinaceus* (dorsal view) (Cassidae)

2. *Casmaria erinaceus* (ventral view)

3. Trumpet shell, *Cymatium lotorium* (Cymatiidae)

4. Trumpet shell, *Distorsio anus* (Cymatiidae)

5. Frog shell, *Bursa rubeta* (Bursidae)

6. Murex shell, *Murex pecten* (Muricidae)

7. Murex shell, *Murex aduncospinosus* (Muricidae)

8. Murex shell, *Haustellum haustellum* (Muricidae)

9. False triton, *Colubraria muricata* (Colubrariidae)

10. Drupe shell, *Drupa ricina* (Thaididae)

11. Drupe shell, *Drupa rubusidaeus* (Thaididae)

12. Drupe shell, *Drupa morum* (Thaididae)

13. Drupe shell, *Drupa rubusidaeus* (variety) (Thaididae)

14. Drupe shell, *Thais armigera* (Thaididae)

15. Murex shell, *Hexaplex cichoreum* (Muricidae)

16. Coral shell, *Rapa rapa* (Coralliophilidae)

17. Coral shell, *Coralliophila radula* (adult) (Coralliophilidae)

18. Coral shell, *Coralliophila neritoidea* (Coralliophilidae)

19. Coral shell, *Coralliophila radula* (juvenile) (Coralliophilidae)

20. Murex shell, *Chicoreus ramosus* (Muricidae)

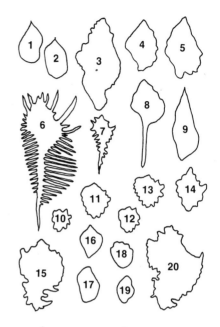

Murex Shells, Etc.

Triton trumpet, *Charonia tritonis* (Ranellidae), 30 cm.

Murex shell, *Murex* sp., (Muricidae), 8 cm.

1. Spindle shell, *Pleuroploca filamentosa* (Fasciolariidae)

2. Dog whelk, *Nassarius papillosus* (Nassariidae)

3. Whelk, *Phos senticosus* (Buccinidae)

4. Whelk, *Cantharus undosus* (Buccinidae)

5. Olive shell, *Oliva caerulea* (Olividae)

6. Spindle shell, *Fusinus colus* (Fasciolariidae)

7. Mitre shell, *Mitra gracilis* (Mitridae)

8. Olive shell, *Oliva erythrostoma* (Olividae)

9. Mitre shell, *Chrysame eremiatrum* (Mitridae)

10. False mitre, *Vexillum coccineum* (Costellariidae)

11. Mitre shell, *Chrysame eremiatrum* (variety) (Mitridae)

12. Mitre shell, *Mitra mitra* (Mitridae)

13. Mitre shell, *Mitra sticta* (Mitridae)

14. Auger shell, *Terebra maculata* (Terebridae)

15. Auger shell, *Terebra crenulata* (Terebridae)

16. Auger shell, *Terebra areolata* (Terebridae)

17. Auger shell, *Terebra dimidiata* (Terebridae)

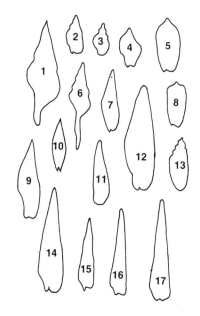

Mitre Shells, Etc.

Olive shell, *Oliva miniacea* (Olividae), 4 cm.

Banded vexillum, *Vexillum taeniatum* (Costellariidae), 6 cm.

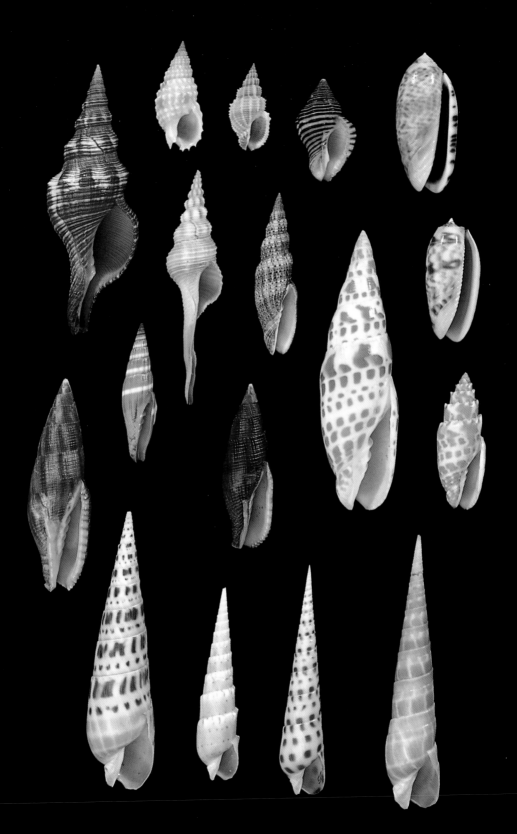

1. *Conus marmoreus*

2. *Conus capitaneus*

3. *Conus flavidus*

4. *Conus vexillum*

5. *Conus stercusmuscarum*

6. *Conus miles*

7. *Conus eburneus*

8. *Conus quercinus*

9. *Conus lividus*

10. *Conus pulicarius*

11. *Conus arenatus*

12. *Conus magus*

13. *Conus rattus*

14. *Conus sulcatus*

15. *Conus suturatus*

16. *Conus terebra*

17. *Conus ochroleucus*

18. *Conus coccineus*

19. *Conus nassatella*

20. *Conus radiatus*

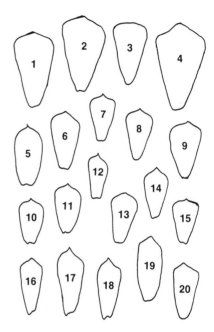

Cone Shells-Conidae

Marmorated cone, *Conus marmoreus*, 6 cm.

Glory-of-the-seas cone, *Conus gloriamaris*, 8 cm.

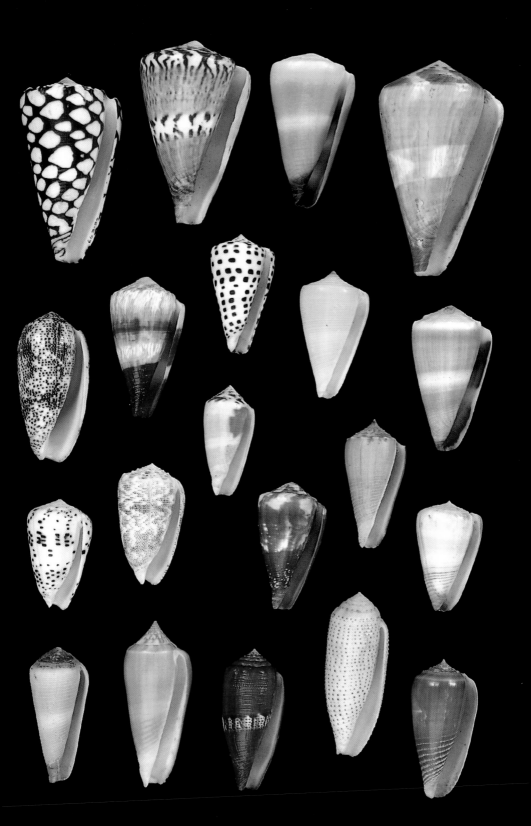

1. *Conus litteratus*

2. *Conus leopardus*

3. *Conus betulinus*

4. *Conus virgo*

5. *Conus imperialis*

6. *Conus generalis*

7. *Conus vitulinus*

8. *Conus striatus*

9. *Conus figulinus*

10. *Conus litoglyphus*

11. *Conus thalassiarchus*

12. *Conus tessulatus*

13. *Conus tulipa*

14. *Conus textile*

15. *Conus episcopus*

16. *Conus aulicus*

17. *Conus geographus*

18. *Conus omaria*

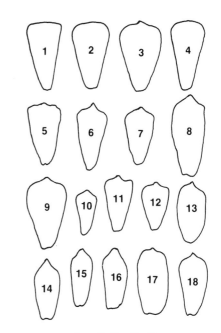

Cone Shells - Conidae

Striated cone, *Conus striatus*, 8 cm.

Geography cone, *Conus geographus*, 10 cm.

Cone Shells – Family Conidae

1.   *Conus rufimaculosus*

2.   *Conus achatinus*

3.   *Conus retifer*

4.   *Conus striatellus*

5.   *Conus planorbis*

6.   *Conus sugillatus*

7.   *Conus musicus*

8.   *Conus sponsalis*

9.   *Conus miliaris*

10.   *Conus ranunculus*

11.   *Conus ebraeus*

12.   *Conus chaldaeus*

13.   *Conus frigidus*

14.   *Conus catus*

15.   *Conus coronatus*

16.   *Conus stramineus*

17.   *Conus caracteristicus*

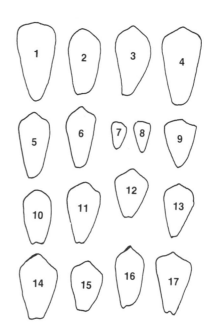

Cone Shells - Conidae

Textile cone, *Conus textile*, 7 cm.

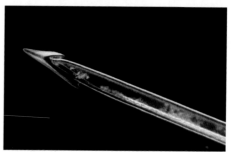

Close-up view of the Textile cone's poisonous dart.

1. Ark Shell, *Barbatia lacerta* (Arcidae)

2. *Barbatia lacerta*

3. Mussel, *Septifer bilocularis* (Mytelidae)

4. *Septifer biocularis*

5. Scallop, *Chlamys pallium* (Pectinidae)

6. *Chlamys pallium*

7. Pearl oyster, *Pteria penguin* (Pteriidae)

8. *Pteria penguin*

9. Scallop, *Chlamys squamosa* (Pectinidae)

10. Pen shell, *Pinna bicolor* (Pinnidae)

11. *Pinna bicolor*

12. Pearl oyster, *Pinctada margaritifera* (Pteriidae)

13. File shell, *Ctenoides ales* (Limidae)

14. Rough cockle, *Chama lazarus* (Chamidae)

15. *Chama lazarus*

16. Tellin shell, *Tellina scobinata* (Tellinidae)

17. *Tellina scobinata*

18. False mussel, *Trapezium oblongum* (Trapeziidae)

19. *Trapezium oblongum*

20. Sunset shell, *Asaphis violascens* (Psammobiidae)

21. *Asaphis violascens*

22. Cardita clam, *Trachycardium orbita* (Carditidae)

23. *Trachycardium orbita*

24. Venus shell, *Periglypta reticulata* (Veneridae)

25. *Periglypta reticulata*

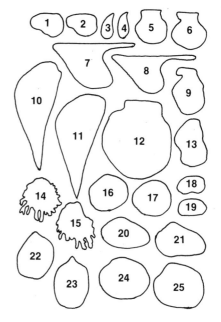

Bivalve Shells

Pearl oyster, *Pinctada margaritifera* (Pteriidae), 15 cm.

Scallop, *Chlamys pallium* (Pectinidae), 12 cm.

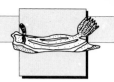

Chapter 12

Nudibranchs and Sea Slugs
Colorful Butterflies of the Reef

If it were not for their small size and inconspicuous habits, the dazzling nudibranchs would certainly be the main attraction on coral reefs. It is well worth the extra effort to search for these stunning creatures. Even an untrained observer can find perhaps 5-10 different types during an average dive or snorkeling session.

Nudibranchs and their snail-related cousins form one of the main divisions (Subclass Opisthobranchia) within the Mollusca. In contrast to gastropod and bivalve molluscs, the evolutionary trend in opisthobranchs has been towards a reduction or even complete loss of the protective shell. Only in the Bubble shells (Cephalaspideans) is this feature still evident. In many marine opisthobranchs, including nudibranchs, the shell is present during the larval stage, but disappears during metamorphosis.

Opisthobranchs are found in nearly all reef habitats. They occur from tide pools down to the greatest depths penetrated by SCUBA divers. They are seen both in the open and under rocks and coral slabs. The key to finding them is to look for their favorite foods. The majority of species feed on algae, sponges, bryozoans, ascidians, and cnidarians (hydroids, anemones, soft corals, gorgonians, etc.). Sea hares (Anaspideans) and Seaweed snails (Sacoglossans) are primarily algal feeders. Compared to most opisthobranchs the Sea hares of the family Aplysiidae are veritable giants. Some species attain a maximum length of between 40 and 50 centimeters.

Nudibranch groups

Most of the colorful opisthobranchs seen on coral reefs belong to the Order Nudibranchia. They are commonly known as nudibranchs. This large group can be divided into four main types (Suborders) on the basis of their general appearance. The Harlequin nudibranchs (Doridaceans) are by far the most numerous. Most are characterized by the combination of a pair of tentacles (rhinophores) on top of the head and a tuft of feathery gills on the rear part of the back. However, certain species, known as phyllidiids, lack conspicuous gills and have lumpy ridges on the back. The Tubercular nudibranchs (Aeolidaceans) are second in abundance and the easiest group to recognize. They are covered with numerous finger-like appendages. The Side-gilled nudibranchs (Dendrotaceans) have several feathery gills along each side of the back, as well as a cup-like sheath around each tentacle on top of the head. The last group, the Veiled nudibranchs (Arminaceans) is characterized by an expanded fleshy lobe on the head and longitudinal ridges along the back.

Clever protection

How do these bright colored, slow-moving creatures escape predators? Nature's ways are frequently ingenious and the protective devices employed by nudibranchs are clever indeed. The flesh of opishthobranchs is frequently toxic or distasteful due to various

◄ *Pleurobranchus forskali* (Pleurobranchidae), 10 cm.

chemical secretions. The bright "poster colored" patterns serve to warn potential predators of their inedible qualities. These colors have most likely evolved in response to the threat of fish predators in view of their intelligence and visual acuity. Once a fish inadvertently samples a sour nudibranch it is not likely to forget this experience. In subsequent encounters the nudibranch's bold color pattern serves to remind the fish of its inedible qualities and it is ignored. Nudibranchs and their relatives also utilize camouflage colors to escape detection. Species found among seaweeds, sponges, and on various cnidarians often effectively blend with the surroundings. The Tubercular nudi-branchs possess a most unusual form of protection. Most species feed on various hydroids and other cnidarians. They are able to ingest the stinging cells (nematocysts) of their prey without firing them. The nematocysts are then incorporated into their own tissue. Thus, the tips of the finger-like projections covering their back, are armed with stolen weapons.

Reproduction

Both sexes are present in a single nudibranch, but self-fertilization does not occur. Special sperm sacs are exchanged during copulation. However, it may take several days, or even weeks before the eggs become fully developed and are actually fertilized. They are deposited in colorful, ribbon-like strands, often on the favored food (ie. algae, sponges, etc.). The veliger larvae is free-swimming in oceanic surface currents for variable periods ranging from a few days to several months. The larval stage can actually be prolonged if the veliger does not come in contact with a shallow reef surface. In many cases metamorphosis into a juvenile does not occur unless the proper feeding surface is encountered.

Chromodoris bullocki (Chromodorididae), 8 cm.

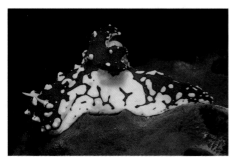

Notodoris gardineri (Aegiridae), 8 cm.

Notodoris sp. (Aegiridae), 8 cm.

Chelidonura electra (Aglajidae), 5 cm.

Chelidonura inornata (Aglajidae), 4 cm.

Philinopsis cyanea (Aglajidae), 5 cm.

Armina sp. (Arminidae), 5 cm.

Dolabella auricularia (Aplysiidae), 30 cm.

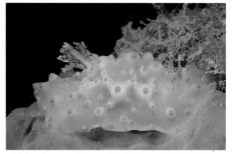

Halgerda aurantiomaculata (Asteronitidae), 6 cm.

Halgerda tessellata (Asteronitidae), 2 cm.

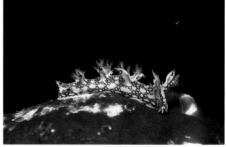

Bornella anguilla (Bornellidae), 3 cm.

Cyerce nigricans (Calliphyllidae), 3 cm.

Ardeadoris egretta (Chromodorididae), 8 cm.

Ceratosoma tenue (Chromodorididae), 6 cm.

Ceratosoma trilobatum (Chromodorididae), 7 cm.

Chromodoris coi (Chromodorididae), 6 cm.

Chromodoris elizabethina (Chromodorididae), 4 cm.

Chromodoris kuniei (Chromodorididae), 6 cm.

Chromodoris magnifica (Chromodorididae), 4 cm.

Chromodoris geometrica (Chromodorididae), 3 cm.

Chromodoris lineolata (Chromodorididae), 6 cm.

Chromodoris sp. (Chromodorididae), 4 cm.

Chromodoris sp. (Chromodorididae), 4 cm.

Glossodoris atromarginata (Chromodorididae), 5 cm.

Mexichromis mariei (Chromodorididae), 5 cm.

Risbecia tryoni (Chromodorididae), 8 cm.

Thurdilla splendida (Elysiidae), 3 cm.

Phyllodesmium briareus (Glaucidae), 5 cm.

Flabellina rubrolineata (Flabellinidae), 3 cm.

Phyllodesmium longicirra (Glaucidae), 12 cm.

Pteraeolidia ianthina (Glaucidae), 12 cm.

Haminoea cymbalum (Haminoeidae), 1 cm.

Hexabranchus sanguineus (Hexabranchidae), 25 cm.

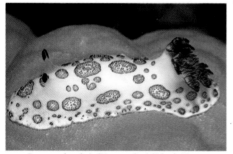

Jorunna funebris (Kentrodorididae), 7 cm.

Kentrodoris rubescens (Kentrodorididae), 16 cm.

Phyllidia coelestis (Phyllidiidae), 8 cm.

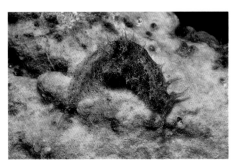

Stylocheilus longicauda (Notarchidae), 5 cm.

Phyllidia coelestis (Phyllidiidae), 7 cm.

Phyllidia ocellata (Phyllidiidae), 5 cm.

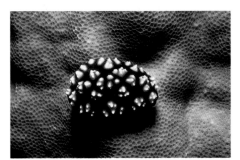

Phyllidia pustulosa (Phyllidiidae), 3 cm.

Phyllidia varicosa (Phyllidiidae), 7 cm.

Phyllidia sp. (Phyllidiidae), 3 cm.

Phyllidiops shiveenoe (Phyllidiidae), 6 cm.

Reticulidia sp. (Phyllidiidae), 3 cm.

Plakobranchus sp. (Plakobranchidae), 3 cm.

Nembrotha kubaryana (Polyceridae), 6 cm.

Nembrotha purpureolineata (Polyceridae), 7 cm.

Gymnodoris celonica (Polyceridae), 5 cm.

Pleurobranchus grandis (Pleurobranchidae), 10 cm.

Pleurobranchus peroni (Pleurobranchidae), 10 cm.

Phestilla melanobranchia (Tergipedidae), 1 cm.

Melibe mirifica (Tethydidae), 12 cm.

Chapter 13

Cephalopods
Keen eyes are watching you!

The octopus and its relatives have the most advanced nervous system of all invertebrate animals. Many of the lower animals are able to detect pressure waves or the difference between shade and sunlight, but none have the keen sense of vision enjoyed by the cephalopods. Their eyes are remarkably human-like and accurately register shapes, textures, and colors. In other words, they see us much the same as we perceive them! The keen eyesight and well developed brain, enable them to deftly catch elusive fish prey. In addition, they feed on crabs, shrimps, and in the case of the octopus, bivalve molluscs.

Cephalopods are a major division (Class) within the Phylum Mollusca. Their name literally means "head-foot" in reference to the two dominant body parts, with "foot" referring to the arms or tentacles. Although outwardly they seem very unique, these animals have the basic molluscan body plan, but with special modifications. While most of us are familiar with the eight-legged octopus, we may need to be introduced to other members of this group, namely cuttlefish, squids, and the chambered nautilus. The latter representative is the most primitive and archaic cephalopod. Its ancestry dates back more than 400 million years to a time when it was the highest form of life in the sea. Today there are only four species of chambered nautilus, which live in deep water, but undergo daily vertical migrations of several hundred meters. Their main distinguishing feature is a coiled multi-chambered shell. It not only protects the nautilus, but also serves to regulate its flotation.

Cuttlefish and squids are perhaps more familiar. Many of you have no doubt sampled these delicacies in restaurants. Both groups are characterized by ten appendages that encircle the mouth. Cuttlefish generally have a stouter body and possess a flat rigid bone dorsally in the mantle cavity. It is commonly found washed ashore on beaches and is sold as cuttlebone in pet shops. Squids have a similar body plan, but are more elongate and lack the cuttlebone. Instead it is replaced by a gelatinous rod known as the gladius.

Enormous diversity

There are about 650-700 species of cephalopods. They inhabit every conceivable undersea habitat. Many live in the open ocean or in abyssal depths. Relatively few species are encountered on coral reefs, but at certain localities they are seen on nearly every dive. Although not found on reefs, the oceanic-dwellling Giant squid has long captured our imagination. This beast grows to a total length of 20 meters and nearly a ton in weight. Fortunately the tropical reef species are considerably smaller, ranging in size from a few centimeters to about 1.5 meters total length for some octopus. Ironically, one of the smallest, the Blue-ringed octopus, has a poisonous bite capable of killing a human. Luckily, it leads a cryptic lifestyle. Normally the toxin is

◄ Undescribed octopus, *Octopus* sp. (Octopodidae), Flores, Indonesia.

used to incapacitate its crab and shrimp prey.

Ink and jet propulsion

Anyone who has observed cephalopods underwater has usually seen them squirt an inky smokescreen. The ink is produced by a gland within the fleshy mantle that encloses the other internal organs. It is ejected during times of stress as a deterrent that helps them to escape from potential predators. The inky blob provides a diversion or at least the vision of the would be predator is temporarily obscured. The ink is ejected from a muscular siphon situated ventrally on the edge of the mantle. The siphon also provides a form of jet locomotion when water is forcibly expelled from the mantle cavity through its opening. Depending on which direction the siphon is pointing, the animal can attain very rapid swimming speeds either forward or backward. Squids and cuttlefish also have membranous lateral fins along the edge of the mantle that are used for stability, steering, and slow swimming.

▼ Nautilus, *Nautilus pompilius* (Nautilidae), 20 cm.

Sex and Growth

Cephalpods, like most higher animals, have separate sexes. The males have a modified arm that functions in the transfer of sperm. The sperm is contained within "packets" that are placed on various parts of the female, depending on the species involved. Actual fertilization does not occur until sometime later when the eggs are being deposited. Squids lay finger-shaped cases filled with clusters of eggs that are attached to rocks, shells, and other debris. Cuttlefish deposit relatively few grape-like eggs amongst bottom growing plants, sponges, or on hard surfaces. Octopus deposit clusters and strands of eggs in rocky crevices and the clutch is guarded until hatching. The incubation period lasts for about 2-3 weeks in most tropical species. Development is direct without any metamorphosis, the young hatching out as miniature adults.

Most reef cephalopods have a very short life span that ranges from about 1-3 years. Besides fishermen, their main enemies are large carnivorous fishes and sharks. Squid and cuttlefish are also consumed regularly by sea birds.

Australian giant cuttlefish, *Sepia apama*, 35 cm.

Broadclub cuttlefish, *Sepia latimanus* , 12 cm.

Bigfin reef squid, *Sepioteuthis lessoniana* (Loliginidae), 20 cm.

Broadclub cuttlefish, *Sepia latimanus*
(Sepiidae), 15 cm.

Pharaoh cuttlefish, *Sepia pharaonis*
(Sepiidae), 35 cm.

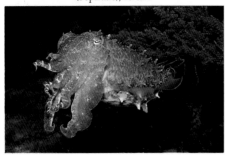

Reef cuttlefish, *Sepia latimanus* (Sepiidae), 40 cm.

Blue-ringed octopus, *Hapalochlaena* sp.
(Octopodidae), 7 cm.

Margined octopus, *Octopus marginatus*, 10 cm.

Common reef octopus, *Octopus cyanea*, 40 cm.

Fijian octopus, *Octopus vitiensis*, 10 cm.

Long-armed octopus, undescribed *Octopus* sp., 10 cm.

Chapter 14

Bryozoans
Colonial Communities

In his classical treatise "Animals without Backbones" author Ralph Buchsbaum refers to bryozoans as one of the animal kingdom's lesser lights. Although it's true they will never win a coral reef popularity contest, these colonial animals are extremely common. The problem is they are frequently mistaken for algae or even sponges. In actual fact, bryozoans constitute a separate major category or phylum. They are one of the most ancient groups of fossil animals, dating back to the early Cambrian period.

Although bryozoans may at first seem inconspicuous, they are not really difficult to find. Look closely and you will see these creatures everywhere ... under stones, wedged between corals and sponges, and in particular on the walls of caves or in shady crevices. They are generally found in colonies attached to the bottom. Each individual is a microscopic animal. It lives in a protective case of calcareous or membranous material. Ciliated tentacles at the anterior end create a current that drives planktonic organisms into the mouth. The ingested food is moved through a U-shaped digestive tract by means of cilia and waste products are expelled from the anus. The latter structure is located near the mouth, but outside of the circle of tentacles. The closeness of mouth and anus may not seem like a good idea, but it's a great arrangement for an animal that lives in a rigid case with only one main opening.

The individual members of the colony are entirely independent of one another, but react in unison, quickly withdrawing into their cases at the slightest vibration. Growth of an individual colony is achieved in plant-like fashion by budding or by sexual reproduction. In some species eggs and sperm are produced by the same animal and shed into the hollow body cavity where fertilization takes place. The larvae are expelled into the surrounding water and are free-swimming until attaching on the bottom where growth of a new colony begins.

Bryozons are generally one of the first group of organisms to colonize a bare rock surface. They have a multitude of growth forms, but those most commonly noticed on coral reefs resemble delicate lace, plant-like branches, or rather thin, sponge-like crusts. Color and growth forms may be extremely variable within a single species, and to a large extent are determined by environmental factors such as current, light availability, and bottom type.

Iodictyum? sp. (Phidoloporidae), 6 cm and *Orthoscuticella?* sp. (Vitaticellidae).

◀ *Iodictyum* sp. or *Triphyllozoon* sp. (Cheilostomata, Phidoloporidae), 6 cm.

Scrupocellaria? sp. (Cheilostomata, Cabereidae), 8 cm.

Iodictyum sp. (Cheilostomata, Phidoloporidae), 12 cm.

Cigclisula sp. (Cheilostomata, Stomachetosellidae), 6 cm.

Cigclisula? sp. (Cheilostomata, Stomachetosellidae), 12 cm.

Reteporellina denticulata (Cheilostomata, Phidoloporidae) 8 cm.

Reteporellina graeffei (Cheilostomata, Phidoloporidae), 6 cm.

Triphyllozoon sp. (Cheilostomata,
Phidoloporidae), 8 cm.

Scrupocellaria maderensis? (Cheilostomata,
Cabereidae). 8 cm

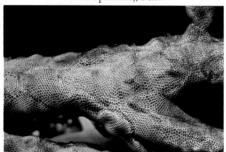

Membranipora sp. (Cheilostomata,
Membraniporidae), 7 cm.

Stylopoma? sp., (Cheilostomata,
Schizoporellidae) 8 cm.

213

Chapter 15

Sea Stars
Spiny Skin and Radial Symmetry

Sea stars or starfish are one of five main groups (Classes) in the phylum Echinodermata. The four related Classes, including brittle stars, sea urchins, sea cucumbers, and feather stars are covered in Chapters 16-19. The Latin name *echinoderm* literally means "spiny-skinned," in reference to the plate-like, calcareous skeleton of these animals.

Sea stars and other echinoderms are characterized by radial symmetry. This design is very obvious in most starfish, in which several arms radiate from a central body mass. Most types typically have five arms, but higher numbers are found in some species. The body actually consists of five equal segments, each containing a duplicate set of various internal organs. The centrally located mouth is situated on the bottom (oral) side of the animal and the anus is on the top (aboral) side. This arrangement reflects their bottom-feeding habits.

Locomotion is generally very slow. It is achieved by means of a remarkable water vascular system, common to all echinoderms. Water is drawn into the system through a sieve plate on the upper surface of the disk. It is conveyed to the individual arms by a series of canals. These in turn are connected to numerous bulb-like apparatus with tubular endings, the tube feet. If you examine the underside of a starfish there is a distinct groove down the center of each arm with tube feet protruding on each side of it. The tube feet, which are equipped with tiny suckers,

are hydraulically expanded and contracted, resulting in the slow movement of the animal.

Amazing regeneration

Starfish are well known for their powers of regeneration. A complete new animal can grow from a small fragment. In some species one of the arms will virtually pull itself away from the body and regenerate. Regenerating starfish are recognized by their lopsided appearance. Sexual reproduction is also evident in this group. Sexes are generally separate and fertilization is external. Huge numbers of eggs are released, but relatively few of the free-swimming larvae survive.

Unusual feeding habits

The diet of starfish is variable depending on the species involved. Many are detritus feeders. They eat the organically enriched film that covers rock, rubble, and sandy surfaces. Others feed on sponges, bryozoans, ascidians, and burrowing molluscs. Species that prey on bivalves are able to literally pry the shells apart by exerting a long steady pull with their tube feet. The mollusc's adductor muscle gradually weakens and the shell pops opens. The starfish then everts its stomach, actually surrounding the edible soft parts with its digestive organs. When the meal is finished the stomach is drawn back into the body. In similar fashion the notorious Crown-of-thorns starfish feeds on live coral polyps.

◄ *Neoferdina offreti* (Ophidiasteridae), 15 cm.

Periodic infestations of this animal have destroyed huge amounts of coral on the Great Barrier Reef and at many other locations.

Starfish and other echinoderms serve as hosts to a variety of symbiotic organisms including shrimps, crabs, parasitic snails, bristle worms, and fishes. The Cushion star (*Culcita*) is sometimes inhabited by a strange transparent fish that actually lives within its gut cavity.

Cardinalfishes (*Siphamia*) are occasionally seen among the spines of the Crown-of-thorns starfish. This relationship is similar to that between anemones and clownfishes.

Most sea stars can be safely handled, but beware of the Crown-of-thorns. It has very sharp, toxic spines that break off and remain embedded in the skin. The wounds can be very painful and medical attention should be obtained.

Crown-of-thorns starfish, *Acanthaster planci* (Acanthasteridae), 30 cm.

Asteropsis carinifera (Asteropseidae), 10 cm.

Astropecten polyacanthus (Astropectinidae), 12 cm.

Echinaster callosus (Echinasteridae), 25 cm.

Echinaster luzonicus (Echinasteridae), 18 cm.

Echinaster luzonicus (Echinasteridae), 30 cm.

Leiaster sp. (Ophidiasteridae), 30 cm.

Tosia queenslandensis (Goniasteridae), 4 cm.

Mithrodia clavigera (Mithrodiidae), 5cm.

Celernia heffernani (Ophidiasteridae), 7 cm.

Fromia indica (Ophidiasteridae), 15 cm.

Fromia monilis (Ophidiasteridae), 12 cm.

Fromia monilis (Ophidiasteridae), 7 cm.

Gomphia gomphia (Ophidiasteridae), 12 cm.

Gomphia rosea?, 20 cm.

Gomphia watsoni, 15 cm.

Linckia laevigata, 25 cm.

Linckia laevigata, 30 cm.

Linckia multiflora, 6 cm.

Linckia guildingii 15 cm.

Nardoa novaecaledoniae, 20 cm.

Neoferdina cumingi, 6 cm.

Cushion star, *Culcita novaguineae* (Oreasteridae), 25 cm.

Choriaster granulatus (Oreasteridae), 30 cm.

Horned sea star, *Protoreaster nodosus* (Oreasteridae), 30 cm.

Protoreaster sp. (Oreasteridae), 30 cm.

Valvaster striatus (Asteropseidae), 4 cm.

Chapter 16

Brittle Stars
Accent on Flexibility

Turn over any large rock or coral slab and there is a good chance you will notice one or more of these fragile, multi-armed creatures scurrying for cover. Brittle stars are close relatives of sea stars, but differ in several important respects. There is no replication of internal organs, just a single set in the clearly delineated central disk. The mouth is situated in the center of the underside of the disc as in sea stars, but there is no separate anus. The highly flexible arms are the most notable feature. They are composed of a series of solid skeletal segments that are sheathed in tissue that resembles muscles and ligaments.

Although they possess a typical echinoderm water vascular system, it is adapted for feeding rather than locomotion. The tube feet lack adhesive suckers. Instead, they produce a slimy mucus that helps to trap microorganisms and detritus. Brittle stars also use their arms to filter planktonic animals and other bits of food from the surrounding current. Sometimes only a few of the arms are extended from its hiding place when feeding in this manner.

Like sea stars, brittle stars can regenerate a new individual from a broken fragment. If touched by a human intruder or fish predator they easily shed parts of their arms or even entire appendages. This is part of their natural defense system. They can move with astonishing quickness, compared to their starfish cousins. Locomotion is actually achieved by vigorous rowing action of the arms.

Baskets and Serpents

Two specialized types of brittle stars are sometimes encountered on coral reefs. Basket stars are easily recognized by their complexly branched arms. These nocturnal animals emerge from daytime hiding places to feed on plankton. They usually occupy a position exposed to strong currents, often on sea fans or other gorgonians. The numerous, highly branched arms form an effective net for trapping a variety of larvae and other plankton. Serpent stars are another modified type of brittle star. They are seen coiled in snake-like fashion around the branches of various gorgonians.

Serpent star, *Astrobrachion adhaerens* (Asteroschematidae), 10 cm.

◄ *Ophiothrix purpurea* (Ophiotrichidae), 20 cm.

Serpent star, *Astrobrachion adhaerens* (Asteroschematidae), 12 cm.

Basket star, *Astroboa granulatus* (Gorgonocephalidae), 80 cm.

Basket star, *Astroboa nuda*, 80 cm.

Unidentified basket star, 45 cm.

Ophiomastix janualis
(Ophiocomidae), 20 cm.

Ophiomastix variabilis
(Ophiocomidae), 20 cm.

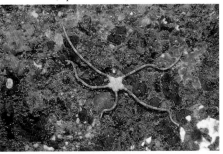

Cryptopelta longibrachialis
(Ophiodermatidae), 20 cm.

Ophiarachna incrassata
(Ophiodermatidae), 30 cm.

Ophiarachnella gorgonia
(Ophiodermatidae), 18 cm.

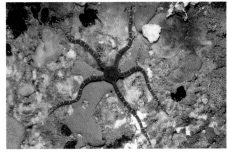

Ophiarachnella septemspinosa
(Ophiodermatidae), 20 cm.

Ophiarachnella sp.
(Ophiodermatidae), 20 cm.

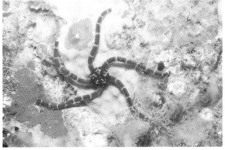

Ophioclastus hataii?
(Ophiodermatidae), 12 cm.

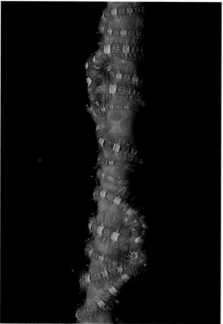

Ophiopeza? sp.(Ophiodermatidae), 15 cm.

Ophiothrix sp. (Ophiotrichidae), 6 cm.

Ophiomyxa australis (Ophiomyxidae), 20 cm.

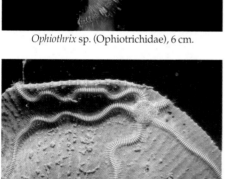

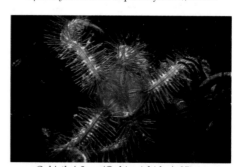

Ophiothrix nereidina (Ophiotrichidae), 25 cm.

Ophiothrix? sp. (Ophiotrichidae), 25 cm.

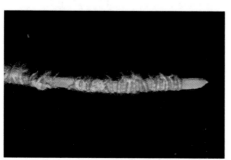

Ophiothela danae (Ophiotrichidae), 6 cm.

Ophiolepis superba (Ophiuridae), 12 cm.

Chapter 17

Feather Stars
Colorful Filter Feeders

Feather stars are one of the most visible members of the reef community. They are especially abundant in areas exposed to periodic strong currents, which convey an abundant supply of planktonic food. Feather stars, also known as crinoids, use special appendages called cirri on the underside of the body to cling to the bottom. They are frequently perched on sponges, gorgonians, and tall coral heads in order to get maximum exposure to the passing current. Although largely immobile, they can use the cirri for crawling and can actually swim by flapping the feathery arms.

Like other echinoderms feather stars have radial symmetry. The numerous arms project from a central disc. One major difference in comparison to sea stars, brittle stars, and sea urchins is related to their planktonic feeding habit. Feather stars filter food from surrounding waters rather than the bottom. Therefore, the mouth is situated on the upper side. The anus, as in starfish, is also on the upper surface, but is located on an elevated cone.

A multitude of arms

The number of arms is variable depending on the species, and may even vary within individual species. Some have only five, others have up to 200. Many of the reef species possess 10-20 arms. Individual arms have numerous, fine, side branches. These are called pinnules and give the animal its feathery appearance. The pinnules are coated with a sticky substance that helps to catch food. Plankton and bits of organic debris are conveyed from the pinnules to the mouth by the motion of tiny hairs that line special food gutters, running down the center of each arm. In some of the larger species that have numerous arms the total length of the food gutters may exceed 100 meters!

Feather stars are primarily nocturnal in habit, although it is not unusual to see them in the open during the day. They are probably opportunistic, feeding when currents are optimum. It would appear these animals would be easy prey for fish predators, but they are largely ignored. They may have skin toxins which serve as a deterrent. The bright colors displayed by many feather stars may in fact signal distasteful qualities.

Colobometra perspinosa (Colobometridae), 25 cm.

◄ *Himerometra bartschi* (Himerometridae), 15 cm.

Pontiometra andersoni (Colobometridae), 20 cm.

Cenometra bella (Colobometridae), 20 cm.

Oligometra serripinna (Colobometridae), 10 cm.

Petasometra clarae (Colobometridae), 10 cm.

Capillaster multiradiatus (Comasteridae), 15 cm.

Comanthina nobilis, 25 cm.

Comanthina audax, 25 cm.

Comanthina schlegelii, 20 cm.

Comanthus alternans, 20 cm.

Comanthus parvicirrus, 20 cm.

Comaster multibrachiatus (Comasteridae), 25 cm.

Comaster multifidus (Comasteridae), 25 cm.

Amphimetra sp. (Himerometridae), 15 cm.

Lamprometra sp. (Mariametridae), 15 cm.

Tropiometra afra (Tropiometridae), 30 cm (L. Vail).

Oxycomanthus bennetti, 20 cm.

Oxycomanthus bennetti, 20 cm.

Himerometra robustipinna (Himerometridae), 20 cm.

Stephanometra sp. (Mariametridae), 20 cm.

Living on a Star

There are numerous examples on the coral reef of animals that live together for the benefit of either one organism or both. Such an association is known as symbiosis. Perhaps the best known example is that which occurs between damselfishes (mainly in the genus *Amphiprion*) and giant sea anemones. Examples of their symbiotic relationship are illustrated in Chapter 25 (pages 308-310). The fish-anemone relationship involves relatively large, readily observable animals, but there are an incredible number of associations containing very small, often cryptic animals. For example, crustaceans frequently live with a variety of other invertebrates and fishes (see Chapter 10). Echinoderms are also prominent hosts of symbiotic animals. Several animals found with feather stars are shown on this page. Shelter and a steady food supply are often the main benefits received by the more mobile partner. The animals featured here probably feed on the microorganisms that are filtered by the feather star.

Crinoid clingfish, *Discotrema crinophila*.

Elegant squat lobster, *Allogalathea elegans*.

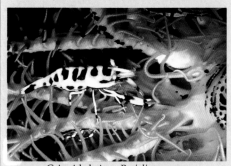

Crinoid shrimp *Periclimenes* sp.

Crinoid brittle star (unidentified).

Chapter 18

Sea Urchins
Nature's Pincushions

Anyone who blunders into a spiny *Diadema* sea urchin is not likely to forget it. The delicate, venomous spines become embedded in the skin and it hurts! Although they should be respected as a potential danger, sea urchins are beautiful, fascinating creatures definitely worth our attention.

Sea urchins have a basic echinoderm body structure including a water vascular system with associated tube feet, and a chitinous skeleton covered with a thin layer of skin. The tube feet function in locomotion as in starfish, but movement is also aided by leverage action of the spines on the underside of the body. As a result they can move much faster than starfish.

Behavior and feeding habits

Sea urchins are generally nocturnal. They spend daylight hours tightly wedged under rocks or in crevices. However, *Diadema* sometimes form aggregations in exposed situations. Both nocturnal and clustering behavior are defense mechanisms for avoiding fish predators. In spite of their sharp spines, urchins are fair game for some fishes, particularly triggerfishes and puffers.

Many species are algal grazers, but others feed on a variety of encrusting organisms, especially sponges, bryozoans, and ascidians. The mouth is centrally located on the underside of the body. It is equipped with well developed jaws and a set of horny teeth. The jaw apparatus is commonly known as "Aristotle's Lantern". As in starfish there is an anal opening on the middle of the upper surface. Some urchins have a

spherical, semi-transparent cloaca, that protrudes from the anal opening. It can be withdrawn into the shell. It probably serves to channel waste products away from the nearby opening of the water vascular system.

The tube feet tend to be longer than those of starfish. They are arranged in five rows between the main joints of the five-plated shell, and are also numerous on the ventral surface. As mentioned above they are used for locomotion, but serve other important functions including respiration, excretion of waste, touch and chemical reception, and are also used for digging.

Sea urchins are basically hollow shells. Very little space is occupied by the internal organs. This allows for the development of the gonads during the breeding season. The body cavity is crammed with eggs or sperm at this time. This is one of the main reasons urchins are so attractive to fish predators. The raw gonads of certain urchins are also considered a great delicacy by the Japanese, who use them in making sushi.

Sand dollars and heart urchins

Most sea urchins are instantly recognizable. However, two specialized types, the sand dollars and heart urchins, have an unusual appearance. The sand dollar has a much flattened, oval shell with a starfish "insignia" on its upper side. Its spines and tube feet are numerous, but very tiny. Heart urchins are oval, somewhat football-shaped, with short bristles covering the body. Both types are pale in color and live under sand.

◄ *Echinothrix calamaris* (Diadematidae), 20 cm.

Prionocidaris verticillata (Cidaridae), 10 cm.

Eucidaris metularia (Cidaridae), 15 cm.

Phyllacanthus imperialis (Cidaridae), 18 cm.

Astropyga radiata (Diadematidae), 20 cm.

Diadema savignyi (Diadematidae), 20 cm.

Diadema setosum (Diadematidae), 20 cm.

Echinothrix calamaris (Diadematidae), 12 cm.

Echinothrix diadema? (Diadematidae), 20 cm.

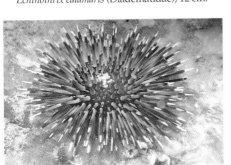

Echinometra mathaei (Echinometridae), 8 cm.

Echinometra sp. (Echinometridae), 8 cm.

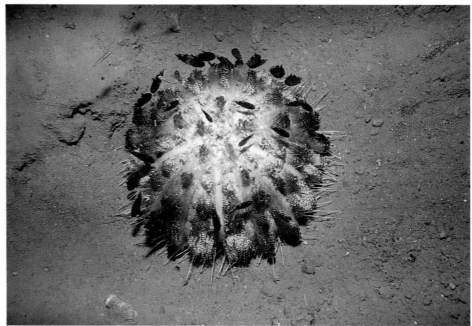

Asthenosoma varium (Echinothuridae), 25 cm and cardinalfish *(Siphamia)*.

Echinostrephus aciculatus
(Echinometridae), 6 cm.

Heterocentrotus mammillatus
(Echinometridae), 15 cm.

Heterocentrotus trigonarius
(Echinometridae), 15 cm.

Parasalenia gratiosa
(Parasaleniidae), 7cm.

Stomopneustes variolaris
(Stomopneustidae), 10 cm.

Mespilia globulus
(Temnopleuridae), 8 cm.

Salmacis belli
(Temnopleuridae), 18 cm.

Tripneustes gratilla
(Toxopneustidae), 12 cm.

Toxopneustes pileolus
(Toxopneustidae), 12 cm.

Brissopsis luzonica
(Brissidae), 5 cm.

Clypeaster oshimensis
(Clypeasteridae), 7 cm.

Lovenia elongata
(Loveniidae), 6 cm.

Chapter 19

Holothurians
The Sand Gobblers

At first glance holothurians and starfish appear to have little in common. But both are types of echinoderms. Unlike other members of this Phylum, holothurians do not have distinct radial symmetry, at least on the outside. Instead, the body is elongate with a head and tail (although the two may be indistinguishable). This body form evolved in response to their peculiar way of life. Most species feed on the rich organic film that coats sandy surfaces. These living "conveyor belts" ingest large amounts of sand as they slowly crawl over the bottom. The edible, organic material is digested as the sand particles pass through the straight, tube-like digestive tract. The processed sand is then expelled from the anus, leaving a characteristic trail on the bottom.

Three basic types are seen in the vicinity of coral reefs: aspidochirotes, dendrochirotes, and apodus holothurians. Those most commonly encountered belong to the first group. They generally have a tubular shape and the body is covered with a thick leathery skin. The tube feet are best developed on the ventral surface and function in locomotion. The tube feet around the mouth region form specialized feeding tentacles that carry sand particles into the mouth. Several species spurt sticky, toxic threads when threatened by predators, or roughly handled by humans.

The dendrochirotes are similar in shape to the aspidochirotes, but have much longer, branched feeding tentacles. These form an effective net for trapping current-borne zooplankton. Although capable of movement with their tube feet, individuals seldom change position.

Apodus holothurians have a thin, sticky outer skin and well developed feeding tentacles. They move by expanding and contracting the body musculature, but also utilize their tube feet. Favored habitats include silt or sand bottoms, and seagrass meadows. Some smaller species also occur on the surface of barrel sponges or other sponge types. Apparently they feed on substances secreted by the sponges as well as surface detritus. Some species of *Synapta*, are veritable giants, reaching a length of slightly over five meters. Most holothurians are considerably smaller, usually ranging from about five to 50 cm in length.

Sea cucumbers

Holothurians are popularly known as sea cucumbers. This name is derived from their widespread use in Asia as a base for soups. Considerable commercial trade is based on several species in the aspidochirote group commonly referred to as trepang or beche-de-mer. The live animals are gathered from the reef and dried in the sun or with special ovens. The leathery skin is transformed to a gelatinous, rather tasteless concoction during the cooking process.

Pentacta crassa? (Cucumariidae), 20 cm.

Holothurians serve as hosts to a variety of symbiotic organisms, particularly crabs, shrimps, and worms. However, the most unusual relationship involves pearlfishes of the family Carapidae. They are commonly found in the Leopard sea cucumber (*Bohadschia argus*). Every specimen we have dissected invariably contained a slender, 5-10 cm, transparent fish in its gut cavity. A few other species are also known to contain fish, including the Prickly sea cucumber (*Thelanota ananas*) and the Spiny Black (*Stichopus chloronotus*). These same fishes also inhabit *Culcita* and *Acanthaster* starfish, as well as pearl-oyster shells. We have never seen a fish outside its host in nature, but have artificially induced them to leave and reenter in an aquarium situation. The fish enters (tail first) and exits through the holothurian's anus. Evidently the fish feeds on the gonads and other tissues of its host.

Cercodemas anceps (Cucumariidae), 20 cm.

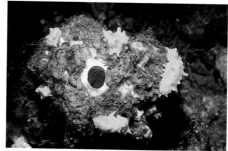

Pentacta lutea? (Cucumariidae), 3 cm.

Pseudocolchirus violaceus (Cucumariidae), 25 cm.

Actinopyga lecanora (Holothuriidae), 30 cm.

Actinopyga lecanora (Holothuriidae), 30 cm.

Actinopyga mauritiana (Holothuriidae), 35 cm.

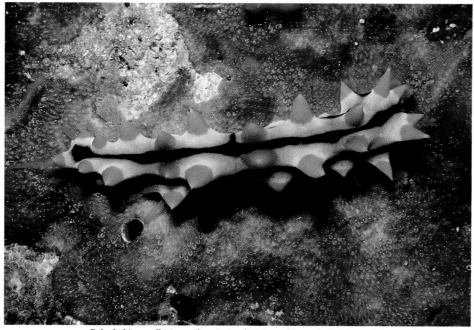

Bohadschia graeffei, juvenile mimic of toxic nudibranch (L. Newman).

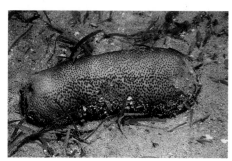

Bohadschia argus, 40 cm.

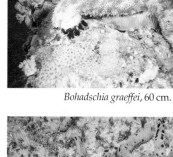

Bohadschia graeffei, 60 cm.

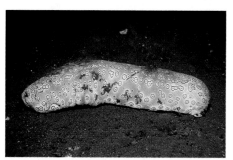

Bohadschia marmorata, 30 cm.

Holothuria atra, 20 cm.

Holothuria fuscogilva?, 30 cm.

Holothuria edulis, 30 cm.

Holothuria fuscopunctata, 40 cm.

Holothuria leucospilota, 50 cm.

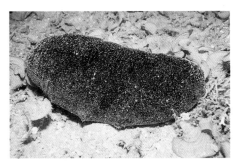

Holothuria nobilis, 30 cm.

Stichopus noctivagus (Stichopodidae), 15 cm.

Labidodemas semperianum (Holothuriidae), 15 cm.

Unidentified species (Holothuriidae?), 25 cm.

Stichopus chloronotus (Stichopodidae), 40 cm.

Stichopus horrens (Stichopodidae), 35 cm.

Thelenota ananas, 50 cm.

Stichopus pseudhorrens, 50 cm.

Thelenota anax, 60 cm.

Undescribed species of *Stichopus* from New Guinea, 30 cm.

Stichopus variegatus, 40 cm.

Thelenota rubralinata (Stichopodidae), 30 cm.

Euapta godeffroyi (Synaptidae), 100 cm.

Synapta maculata (Synaptidae), 140 cm.

Synapta? sp. (Synaptidae), 100 cm.

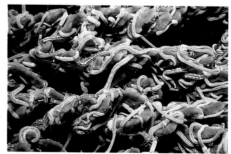

Synaptula sp. (Synaptidae), 10 cm.

Chapter 20

Ascidians
Efficient and Colorful Filters

Ascidians or sea squirts are common in all marine habitats, fixed to rocks, weeds, in caves, on harbor installations and on sandy and muddy substrates. They are members of the Phylum Chordata. Although superficially they appear to have little in common with vertebrates, their larval tail is strengthened with a rod of cells just like the embryonic backbone of a vertebrate; and like the gills of fish, the pharynx of an ascidian is perforated.

Ascidians occur as solitary individuals (up to 20 cm) or as colonies of minute (sometimes only 1 or 2 mm long) zooids. Their bodies are surrounded by, or embedded in, fibrous cellulose-like material, which is sometimes firm and jelly-like, or delicate and membranous, or even tough and leathery with weeds, sponges and other ascidians growing on it. Often it contains pigments and is brightly colored. Sometimes green symbiotic algae are embedded in it.

Colonies are of every conceivable shape and form...regular and irregular, flat plates or sheets, stalked or sessile, upright flasks, lamellae, cones, or spheres. Sometimes zooids are completely embedded in the matrix, sometimes only partly embedded, and sometimes joined to one another at their base, or to creeping basal stalks. Colonies grow larger as the zooids in them replicate or clone themselves by dividing or budding. Very occasionally the colonies themselves will subdivide. Solitary individuals just grow larger in the usual way.

All ascidians have two apertures...a mouth, or incurrent aperture, and an excurrent one. When undisturbed both apertures are wide open. A continuous stream of water is drawn in through the mouth and is expelled out through the smaller excurrent aperture. This water current is generated by the beating of tiny hairs (cilia) that line the pharynx and its perforations. Food particles, including bacteria and phytoplankton, are filtered from the water as it passes through the pharynx. Gametes and waste products are dispersed in the excurrent stream. Instead of opening directly to the exterior, the excurrent openings of many colonial species are in large internal spaces or canals in the colony matrix. These have only single openings, often on top of the colony where passing currents rapidly disperse the excurrent water.

All solitary forms are externally fertilized. Tadpole-like larvae develop in the plankton. After less than 6 hours, they attach themselves to a substrate, absorb their tail and develop into a juvenile ascidian. Colonial species are internally fertilized, although it is not known yet how the sperm enters the parent zooid without being caught as food. Embryos are incubated in the parent zooid, or in the matrix, and are released only when they have become tailed larvae. They are free swimming for only 10 minutes to one hour before they metamorphose.

◀ Ascidian colony, *Ecteinascidia*? sp. (Perophoridae), Flores, Indonesia.

Phallusia julinea (Ascidiidae), 8 cm.

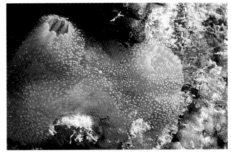

Phallusia julinea (Ascidiidae), 5 cm.

Clavelina moluccensis (Clavelinidae), colony width 12 cm.

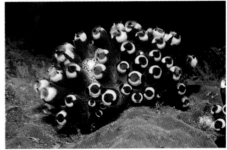

Clavelina robusta (Clavelinidae), colony width 6 cm.

Clavelina sp. (Clavelinidae), colony width 10 cm.

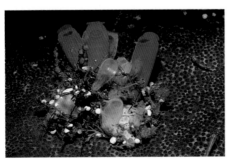

Rhopalaea crassa (Diazonidae), 4 cm.

Rhopalaea crassa (Diazonidae), 4 cm.

Didemnum molle (Didemnidae), 2 cm.

Rhopalaea crassa (Diazonidae), 4 cm.

Didemnum molle (green) and *Didemnum* sp. (orange) colony width 10 cm.

Atriolum robustum (Didemnidae), colonies each about 2 cm diameter.

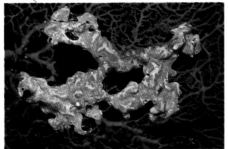

Didemnum sp. (Didemnidae), colony width 15 cm.

Diplosoma similis (Didemnidae), colony width 5 cm.

Diplosoma virens (Didemnidae), actual size.

Lissoclinum patella (Didemnidae), colony width 12 cm.

Unidentified ascidian, possibly Didemnidae, 10 cm width.

Distaplia? sp. (Holozoidae), colony width 8 cm.

Unidentified ascidian (Holozoidae), colony width 30 cm.

Ecteinascidia bandaensis (Perophoridae), actual size.

Eudistoma laysani (Polycitoridae), colony
width 12 cm.

Eudistoma sp. (Polycitoridae), colony
width 10 cm.

Polycitor annulus (Polycitoridae), 3 cm.

Polycitor? sp. (Polycitoridae), 10 cm.

Polycitorella? sp. (Polycitoridae), 8 cm.

Aplidium sp. (Polyclinidae), 7 cm.

Aplidium sp. (Polyclinidae), 10 cm.

Aplidium? sp. (Polyclinidae), colony width 12 cm.

Unidentified ascidian (Polyclinidae?), colony width 10 cm.

Pycnoclavella detorta? (Pycnoclavellidae), 10 cm.

Pycnoclavella diminuta (Pycnoclavellidae), actual size.

Pycnoclavella? sp. (Pycnoclavellidae), actual size.

Botrylloides leachi (Styelidae), colony width 10 cm.

Botrylloides leachi (Styelidae), colony width 10 cm.

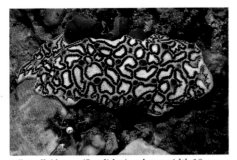

Botrylloides sp. (Styelidae), colony width 10 cm.

Eusynstyela sp. (Styelidae), colony width 12 cm.

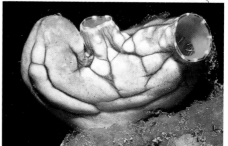

Polycarpa aurata, 8 cm.

Cnemidocarpa stolonifera, 8 cm.

Polycarpa clavata, 12 cm.

Symplegma sp., colony width 15 cm.

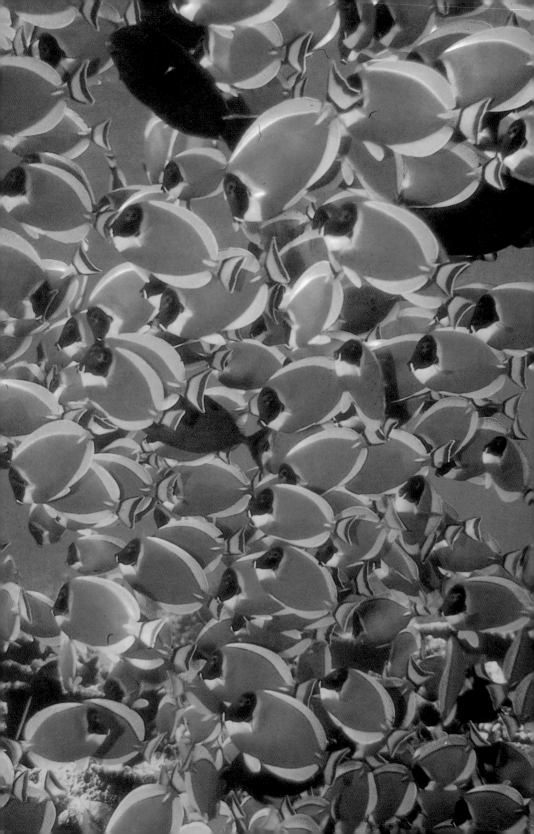

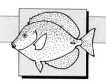

Chapter 21

Fishes
Heart and Soul of the Coral Reef

Fishes are the coral reef's most conspicuous inhabitants. In essence they are its personality. It's easy to quickly assess the richness of a particular dive site. When there is a multitude of rainbow-hued fishes a favorable impression is immediately conveyed.

More species are found on tropical reefs than any other aquatic environment. Of an estimated 12,000 marine fishes, perhaps as many as 7,000 occur on coral reefs or nearby inshore habitats. At first glance the abundance of fishes on a coral reef seems staggering. Indeed, in certain areas one may find as many as 300 different types inhabiting a small plot of reef. But don't despair. It is well within everyone's capability to become familiar with the majority of the reef's fishes, at least at the family level (see box - The Big Ten).

Fish-watching is the aquatic counterpart of bird-watching and a basic knowledge of common reef fishes can add considerable enjoyment to your diving activities. You may wish to use your knowledge of fish identification in compiling a checklist of what you have seen on your dives or in labeling your underwater photos.

Every fish on the reef has an interesting story to tell. Watch them carefully. You can learn a great deal of their habits and way of life. Small damselfishes are everywhere and it is easy to observe spawning and nest guarding in many species. Colorful clownfishes (also belonging to the damselfish family) live among the tentacles of large sea anemones. They are immune from the stinging tentacles of their host due to a special chemical additive in their external body slime.

In spite of the first impression of mass confusion there is a great deal of order in the fish community. Each species has a specialized role in the complex reef ecosystem. This role is defined by various physical and biological parameters. For example, a certain type of plankton-feeding goby may be found only on steep outer reef slopes in a restricted depth zone where currents are optimal for providing the necessary food supply. This particular goby might also be restricted to living on the surface of a certain type of sponge or sea whip. The Urchin clingfish (page 264) is always found among the spines of *Diadema* sea urchins or in nearby coral. It obtains nourishment from feeding on the tubefeet of the urchin and also coral-burrowing molluscs.

The keen-eyed observer will often notice the same fishes on repeated visits to a particular reef. Most fishes do not wander aimlessly from one reef to the next. They are either territorial or home ranging. Territorial species, such as many damselfishes, zealously guard a small plot of turf, perhaps a square meter in area. In this way they have control over their algal food supply and also there is a private nesting site available. The territorial fishes are selective when guarding their property. They often exhibit the most aggression towards others of their own species and fishes that might rob their food supply. This aggressiveness is particularly enhanced during reproductive periods. For example, damselfishes will attack egg-eating wrasses and butterflyfishes with a vengeance. As a rule many of the reef's tiny inhabitants, such as gobies, blennies, and triplefins are somewhat territorial. Even fish that do not maintain a

◄ School of Powder-blue surgeonfishes, *Acanthurus leucosternon*, Maldive Islands.

strict territory are generally confined to a particular section of the reef, which is its feeding ground or home range.

Sex life of a fish

Most reef fishes are egg layers. Wrasses, parrotfishes, butterflyfishes, and many other families scatter their eggs in open water. Spawning frequently occurs at dusk and may be preceded by much rapid swimming and chasing. It is common to witness both pair and group spawning. A spawning event often culminates when the participants rise rapidly towards the surface and then abruptly swim back towards the bottom, releasing eggs and sperm at the apex of the ascent.

Another reproductive mode involves species that lay their eggs on the bottom, frequently in rocky crevices, empty shells, sandy depressions, or on the surface of invertebrates such as sponges, corals, or gorgonians. Among the best known fishes in this category are the damselfishes, gobies, and triggerfishes. They usually prepare the surface prior to egg deposition by clearing detritus and algal growth. Bottom spawners also have elaborate courtship behavior involving aggressive chasing and fin erection displays. This behavior has been extensively studied in damselfishes. One or both parents usually care for the nest of eggs until hatching.

A very specialized reproductive mode is seen in cardinalfishes. The male incubates the egg mass in its mouth. Similarly, pipefishes and seahorses brood their eggs on a highly vascularized region of the belly or underside of the tail. The eggs of these fishes and the various bottom spawners are generally larger, less numerous, have a longer incubation period, and are more advanced when hatched compared to the eggs and larvae of open-water spawners. Hatching may take up to one week (in clownfishes for example) and the larvae then live in

Damselfishes (mainly *Chromis viridis*), Indonesia.

the open sea for up to several weeks before settling on the bottom in a suitable reef habitat.

How long do reef fishes live?

There is very little information on the longevity of most reef fishes. One of the longest recorded life spans is that of the Lemon shark, which may reach 50 years. Most of the larger reef sharks probably live at least to an age of 20-30 years. In general larger reef fishes such as groupers, snappers, and emperors tend to live longer than smaller species. Otolith (ear bone) aging techniques indicate that some groupers live at least 25 years and some snappers approximately 20 years. Most of our knowledge of smaller reef fishes has resulted from aquarium studies. The values obtained from captive fishes may exceed the natural life span due to lack of predation and abundance of food. Batfishes (*Platax*) are known to survive for 20 years and even small species such as damselfishes and angelfishes may reach 10 years or more.

The Big Ten

Surprisingly the bulk of fishes on a typical coral reef belong to relatively few families. Collectively the ten most abundant families constitute as much as 60-70 percent of all fishes at a particular locality. After only a few dives or snorkeling sessions it is easy to recognize them, principally on the basis of shape, general color pattern themes, and behavior. Here is a capsule summary of the dominant families:

Damselfishes (Pomacentridae)- Perhaps the most conspicuous inhabitants of the reef. They form large plankton-feeding schools above the reef. Other bottom-dwelling species occupy territories that blanket the reef's surface. Spawning activity is readily observable. The male parent guards a nest of eggs (often on rocky bottom) during a 2-7 day incubation period. **Pages 307 - 316.**

Wrasses (Labridae)- These colorful fishes inhabit all reef environments. They feed mainly on small invertebrates, either on the bottom or in midwater. They usually spawn at dusk either in pairs or in groups that are dominated by one or more gaudily colored males. The numerous tiny eggs rise to the surface and are not cared for by the parents. Most wrasses are capable of female to male sex change. **Pages 320 - 326.**

Butterflyfishes (Chaetodontidae)- Renowned for their exquisite color patterns and graceful appearance. They are perhaps the best known of all reef fishes. Many of the species feed partly or exclusively on live corals. They are often seen in pairs, which scientific studies have revealed are permanent lifetime bonds. **Pages 295 - 302.**

Angelfishes (Pomacanthidae)- Close relatives of the butterflyfishes and equally beautiful. The larger species are prime targets for fish-watchers and photographers. They feed on sponges and small invertebrates. The large angel species produce a loud drumming noise when agitated. **Pages 302 - 306.**

Cardinalfishes (Apogonidae)- The nocturnal counterpart of damselfishes in terms of sheer abundance. During the day some species form huge resting aggregations around coral formations. Others retire in caves and crevices. At night they actively feed on small shrimps and crabs. Males incubate the female's egg mass in their mouth. **Pages 279 - 281.**

Groupers and Basslets (Serranidae)- This large diverse group includes some of the reefs largest fishes. The giant Queensland Grouper grows to 270 cm and over 400 kg. The family also includes the dainty and brightly colored fairy basslets or Anthias, which are particularly common on outer reefs and drop-offs. Sex change from female to male is found in most species. **Pages 271 - 276.**

Parrotfishes (Scaridae)- Close relatives of the wrasses and one of the dominant algal-feeding families. Juveniles and females are generally drab in comparison to the gaudily colored terminal phase males. Individuals are capable of female to male sex change. They consume considerable amounts of coral rock while feeding. It is ground to a fine powder by special teeth in the throat and voided with the feces. Spawning is similar to that of wrasses. **Pages 327 - 328.**

Surgeonfishes (Acanthuridae)- Often seen in schools, sometimes containing several species. They graze on the filamentous algal mat that covers the reef. Avoid handling these fishes as they possess a sharp scalpel-like structure on each side of the tail base. **Pages 336 - 339.**

Blennies (Blenniidae)- Small territorial bottom dwellers. They are seen solitarily or in small groups. Eggs are laid in crevices, under rocks, or in abandoned shells and worm tubes. The male guards them until hatching . **Pages 330 - 331.**

Gobies (Gobiidae)- Last but not least, these small bottom-living fishes are actually the most abundant of all reef fishes in terms of number of species. But they are easily overlooked due to their diminutive size (many are under 4-5 cm) and cryptic habits. Look closely at the surface of rocks, sponges, and corals and you will begin to appreciate the diversity of this interesting group. Some of the most beautiful members of the family share their sandy burrows with shrimps. Spawning habits are similar to those of blennies. **Pages 332 - 334.**

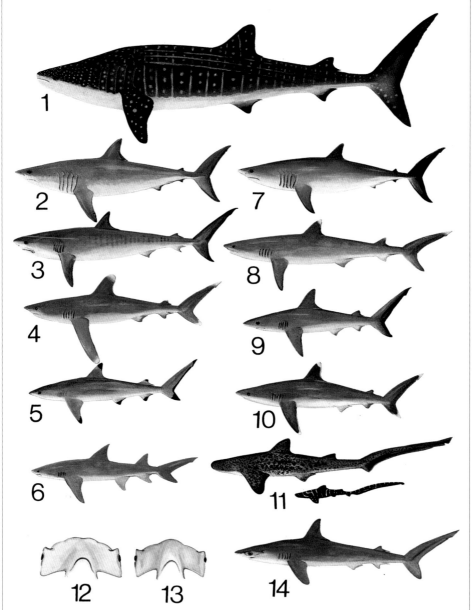

1) Whale shark *(Rhincodon typus)*; 2) Great white *(Carcharodon carcharias)*; 3) Tiger *(Galeocerdo cuvier)*;
4) Oceanic whitetip *(Carcharhinus longimanus)*; 5) Blacktip *(Carcharhinus melanopterus)*;
6) Lemon shark *(Negaprion acutidens)*; 7) Mako *(Isurus oxyrinchus)*; 8) Reef whitetip *(Triaenodon obesus)*;
9) Grey reef *(Carcharhinus amblyrhynchos)*; 10) Silvertip *(Carcharhinus albimarginatus)*; 11) Leopard
shark, adult and juvenile *(Stegostoma fasciatum)*; 12 &14) Scalloped hammerhead *(Sphyrna lewini)*;
13) Smooth hammerhead *(Sphyrna zygaena)*.

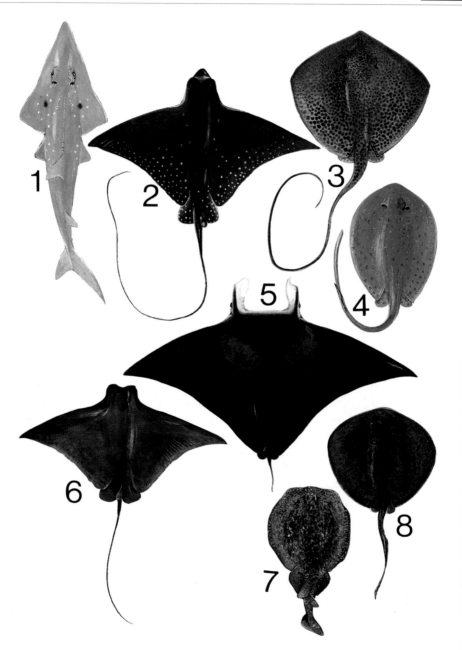

1) Shovelnose ray *(Rhyncobatus djiddensis)*; 2) Spotted eagle ray *(Aetobatus narinari)*;
3) Coachwhip ray *(Himantura uarnak)*; 4) Blue-spotted ray *(Taeniura lymma)*;
5) Manta ray *(Manta birostris)*; 6) Cownose ray *(Rhinoptera neglecta)*;
7) Electric ray *(Torpedo fuscomaculata)*; 8)Black-blotched ray *(Taeniura melanospila)*.

Starry moray, *Echidna nebulosa*, 50 cm.

Black-spotted moray, *Gymnothorax tessellata*, 200 cm.

Giant moray, *Gymnothorax javanicus*, 250 cm.

Yellow-margined moray, *Gymnothorax flavimarginatus*, 150 cm.

Whitemouth moray, *Gymnothorax meleagris*, 100 cm.

Undulated moray, *Gymnothorax undulatus*, 100 cm.

Ribbon eel, *Rhinomuraena quaesita*, adult female, 100 cm. Males/juveniles with black body.

Grey eel, *Siderea grisea*, 50 cm.

Crocodile snake eel, *Brachysomophis crocodilinus*, 130 cm.

Marbled snake eel, *Callechelys marmorata*, 100 cm.

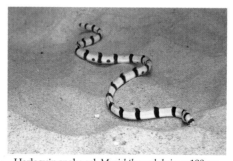

Harlequin snake eel, *Myrichthys colubrinus*, 100 cm.

Spotted snake eel, *Myrichthys maculosus*, 100 cm.

Spotted garden eel, *Heteroconger hassi*
(Heterocongridae), 40 cm.

Striped catfish, *Plotosus lineatus* (Plotosidae), juveniles, 8 cm.

Reef lizardfish, *Synodus variegatus* (Synodontidae), 14 cm.

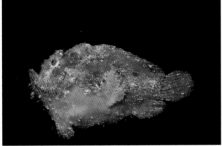

Anglerfish, *Antennarius coccineus* (Antennariidae), 6 cm.

Sargassum anglerfish, *Histrio histrio* (Antennariidae), 10 cm.

Urchin clingfish, *Diademichthys lineatus* (Gobiesocidae), 4 cm.

Crocodile needlefish, *Tylosaurus crocodilus* (Belonidae), 80 cm.

Shadowfin soldierfish, *Myripristis adusta* (Holocentridae), 15 cm.

Bigscale soldierfish, *Myripristis berndti* (Holocentridae), 22 cm.

Lattice soldierfish, *Myripristis violacea*, 15 cm.

Whitetip soldierfish, *Myripristis vittata*, 15 cm.

Spotfin squirrelfish, *Neoniphon sammara*, 20 cm.

Tailspot squirrelfish, *Sargocentron caudimaculatum*, 16 cm.

Crown squirrelfish, *Sargocentron diadema*, 12 cm.

Blackspot squirrelfish, *Sargocentron melanospilos*, 20 cm.

Seychelles squirrelfish, *Sargocentron seychellense*, 20 cm (W. Indian Ocean).

Sabre squirrelfish, *Sargocentron spiniferum*, 30 cm.

Smooth flutemouth, *Fistularia commersonii* (Fistulariidae), 100 cm.

Razorfish, *Aeoliscus strigatus* (Centriscidae), 10 cm.

Trumpetfish, *Aulostomus chinensis* (Aulostomidae), 40 cm.

Harlequin ghost pipefish, *Solenostomus paradoxus* (Solenostomidae), 10 cm.

Banded pipefish, *Corythoichthys intestinalis*, 10 cm.

Ringed pipefish, *Doryrhamphus dactyliophorus*, 12 cm.

Bluestripe pipefish, *Doryrhamphus excisus*, 6 cm.

Spotted seahorse, *Hippocampus kuda*, 12 cm.

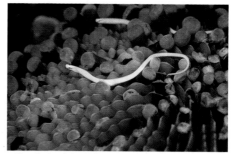

Coral pipefish, *Siokunichthys nigrolineatus*, 8 cm.

Cockatoo waspfish, *Ablabys taenianotus*, 8 cm.

Twinspot lionfish, *Dendrochirus biocellatus*, 12 cm.

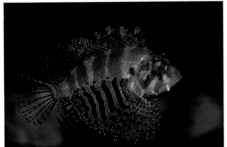

Dwarf lionfish, *Dendrochirus brachypterus*, 12 cm.

Zebra lionfish, *Dendrochirus zebra*, 16 cm.

Ragged-finned firefish, *Pterois antennata*, 15 cm.

Hawaiian lionfish, *Pterois sphex*, 8 cm (J. Randall).

Red firefish, *Pterois volitans*, 28 cm.

Guam scorpionfish, *Scorpaenodes guamensis*, 12 cm.

Estuarine stonefish, *Synanceia horrida*, 26 cm.

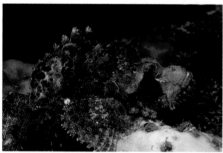

Smallscale scorpionfish, *Scorpaenopsis oxycephalus*, 20 cm.

Smallscale scorpionfish, *Scorpaenopsis oxycephalus*, 22 cm.

Yellow-spotted scorpionfish, *Sebastapistes cyanostigma*, 6 cm.

Leaf scorpionfish, *Taenianotus triacanthus*, 8 cm.

Giant flathead, *Cymbacephalus beauforti*, 75 cm.

Goldback anthias, *Pseudanthias evansi*, male, 10 cm (Indian Ocean).

Redfin anthias, *Pseudanthias dispar*, male, 7 cm (W. Pacific).

Stocky anthias, *Pseudanthias hypselosoma*, male, 10 cm.

Squarespot anthias, *Pseudanthias pleurotaenia*, male, 12 cm (W. Pacific).

Squarespot anthias, *Pseudanthias pleurotaenia*, female, 12 cm (W. Pacific).

Purple anthias, *Pseudanthias tuka*, male, 10 cm (W. Pacific).

Scalefin anthias, *Pseudanthias squamipinnis*,
male, 10 cm.

Scalefin anthias, *Pseudanthias squamipinnis*,
female, 8 cm.

Purple anthias, *Pseudanthias tuka*, female,
8 cm (W. Pacific).

Threadfin anthias, *Nemanthias carberryi*,
12 cm (W. Indian Ocean)

Redmouth grouper, *Aethaloperca rogaa*, 25 cm.

White-lined grouper, *Anyperodon leucogrammicus*, 30 cm.

Peacock grouper, *Cephalopholus argus*, 30 cm.

Brown-barred grouper, *Cephalopholis boenak*, 20 cm.

Leopard grouper, *Cephalopholis leopardus*, 18 cm.

Coral grouper, *Cephalopholis miniata*, 30 cm.

Sixspot grouper, *Cephalopholis sexmaculata*, 12 cm.

Tomato grouper, *Cephalopholis sonnerati*, 40 cm.

Flagtail grouper, *Cephalopholis urodeta*, 24 cm.

Barramandi cod or Polkadot grouper
Cromileptes altivelis, 40 cm.

White-spotted grouper, *Epinephelus caeruleopunctatus*, 40 cm.

Blue Maori grouper, *Epinephelus cyanopodus*, 40 cm (W. Pacific).

Black-tipped grouper, *Epinephelus fasciatus*, 28 cm.

Hexagon grouper, *Epinephelus hexagonatus*, 28 cm.

Giant or Queensland grouper, *Epinephelus lanceolatus*, 180 cm.

Trout grouper, *Epinephelus maculatus*, 12 cm (W. Pacific).

Potato grouper, *Epinephelus tukula*, 140 cm.

Dwarf-spotted grouper, *Epinephelus merra*, 18 cm.

Camouflage grouper, *Epinephelus polyphekadion*, 40 cm.

Thinspine grouper, *Gracila albomarginata*, 35 cm.

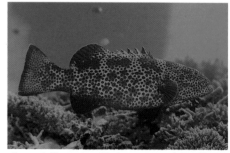

Squaretail grouper, *Plectropomus areolatus*, 40 cm.

Chinese grouper, *Plectropomus laevis*, 50 cm.

Coral trout or Leopard grouper, *Plectropomus leopardus*, 50 cm (W. Pacific).

Barred-cheek grouper, *Plectropomus maculatus*, 50 cm (W. Pacific).

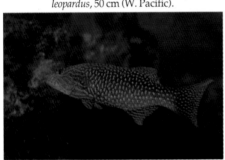

Highfin grouper, *Plectropomus oligocanthus*, 50 cm (W. Pacific).

Coronation grouper, *Variola louti*, 50 cm.

Barred soapfish, *Diploprion bifasciatum*
(Serranidae), 20 cm (W. Pacific).

Sixline soapfish, *Grammistes sexlineatus*
(Serranidae), 15 cm.

Spotted soapfish, *Pogonoperca punctata*
(Serranidae), 20 cm.

Arrowhead soapfish, *Belonoperca chabanaudi*
(Serranidae), 12 cm.

Lined dottyback, *Labracinus lineatus*
(Pseudochromidae), 20 cm (W. Australia only).

Purpleback dottyback, *Pseudochromis diadema*
(Pseudochromidae), 5 cm (W. Pacific).

Yellowback dottyback, *Pseudochromis flavivertex*
(Pseudochromidae), 5 cm (Red Sea).

Fridman's dottyback, *Pseudochromis fridmani*
(Pseudochromidae), 5 cm (Red Sea).

Royal dottyback, *Pseudochromis paccagnellae* (Pseudochromidae), 6 cm (W. Pacific).

Purple dottyback, *Pseudochromis porphyreus* (Pseudochromidae), 5 cm (W. Pacific).

Spendid dottyback, *Pseudochromis splendens* (Pseudochromidae), 6 cm (W. Pacific).

Comet, *Calloplesiops altivelis* (Plesiopidae), 14 cm.

Crescent grunter, *Terapon jarbua* (Terapontidae), 18 cm.

Fiveband flagtail, *Kuhlia mugil* (Kuhliidae), 14 cm.

Bloch's bigeye, *Priacanthus blochii* (Priacanthidae), 25 cm.

Crescent-tail bigeye, *Priacanthus hamrur* (Priacanthidae), 25 cm.

Split-banded cardinalfish, *Apogon compressus*, 9 cm (W. Pacific).

Ring-tailed cardinalfish, *Apogon aureus*, 10 cm.

Three-saddle cardinalfish, *Apogon bandanensis*, 7 cm.

Yellow-striped cardinalfish, *Apogon cyanosoma*, 7 cm.

Spur-cheek cardinalfish, *Apogon fraenatus*, 8 cm.

Narrow-lined cardinalfish, *Archamia fucata*, 8 cm.

Iridescent cardinalfish, *Apogon kallopterus*, 10 cm.

Threadfin cardinalfish, *Apogon leptacanthus*, 5 cm.

Blackstripe cardinalfish, *Apogon nigrofasciatus*, 8 cm.

Nine-banded cardinalfish, *Apogon novemfasciatus*, 8 cm (mainly W. Pacific).

Coral cardinalfish, *Sphaeramia nematoptera*, 6 cm (W. Pacific).

Girdled cardinalfish, *Archamia zosterophora*, 7 cm (W. Pacific).

Tiger cardinalfish, *Cheilodipterus macrodon*, 12 cm.

Five-lined cardinalfish, *Cheilodipterus quinquelineatus*, 10 cm.

Orbicular cardinalfish, *Sphaeramia orbicularis*, 8 cm (W. Pacific).

Flagtail blanquillo, *Malacanthus brevirostris*, 25 cm.

Blue blanquillo, *Malacanthus latovittatus*, 30 cm.

Bigeye trevally, *Caranx sexfasciatus*, 70 cm (P. Kuhn).

Thicklip trevally, *Carangoides orthogrammus*, 40 cm.

Giant trevally, *Caranx ignobilis*, 120 cm.

Bluefin trevally, *Caranx melampygus*, 40 cm.

Golden trevally, *Gnathodon speciosus*, 60 cm.

Yellowtail kingfish, *Seriola lalandi*, 80 cm.

Almaco jack, *Seriola rivoliana*, 85 cm.

Mangrove jack, *Lutjanus argentimaculatus*, 80 cm.

Two-spot snapper, *Lutjanus biguttatus*, 20 cm
(W. Pacific).

Red bass, *Lutjanus bohar*, 60 cm.

Blackspot snapper, *Lutjanus fulviflamma*, 30 cm.

Yellow-margined snapper, *Lutjanus fulvus*, 20 cm.

Paddletail snapper, *Lutjanus gibbus*, 35 cm.

Onespot snapper, *Lutjanus monostigma*, 40 cm.

Scribbled snapper, *Lutjanus rivulatus*, 50 cm.

Yellowstripe snapper, *Lutjanus kasmira*, 30 cm.

Red emperor, *Lutjanus sebae*, 38 cm.

Black and white snapper, *Macolor niger*, 12 cm.

Sailfin snapper, *Symphorichthys spilurus*, 30 cm (W. Pacific).

Chinamanfish, *Symphorus nematophorus*, 25 cm (W. Pacific).

285

Gold-banded fusilier, *Caesio caerularea*, 24 cm.

Red-bellied fusilier, *Caesio cuning*, 25 cm.

Lunar fusilier, *Caesio lunaris*, 30 cm.

Blue and gold fusilier, *Caesio teres*, 30 cm.

Yellowback fusilier, *Caesio xanthonota*, 30 cm
(mainly Indian Ocean).

Wideband fusilier, *Pterocaesio lativittata*, 25 cm.

Neon fusilier, *Pterocaesio tile*, 25 cm.

Common mojarra, *Gerres argyreus*
(Gerreidae), 18 cm.

Painted sweetlips, *Diagramma pictum*, 60 cm.

Painted sweetlips, *Diagramma pictum*, juvenile, 6 cm.

Many-spotted sweetlips, *Plectorhinchus chaetodontoides*, 40 cm (mainly W. Pacific).

Many-spotted sweetlips, *Plectorhinchus chaetodontoides*, juvenile, 6 cm (mainly W. Pacific).

Diagonal-banded sweetlips, *Plectorhinchus lineatus*, 40 cm (W. Pacific).

Oriental sweetlips, *Plectorhinchus orientalis*, 40 cm.

Brown sweetlips, *Plectorhinchus gibbosus*, 40 cm.

Dotted sweetlips, *Plectorhinchus picus*, 35 cm.

Emperors – Family Lethrinidae

Gold-lined sea bream, *Gnathodentex aurolineatus*, 25 cm.

Yellow-spotted emperor, *Lethrinus erythracanthus*, 50 cm.

Thumbprint emperor, *Lethrinus harak*, 35 cm.

Long-nosed emperor, *Lethrinus olivaceus*, 40 cm.

Big-eye bream, *Monotaxis grandoculis*, 30 cm.

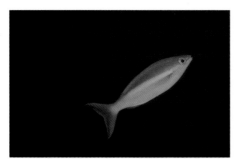

Small-toothed whiptail, *Pentapodus caninus*, 15 cm (W. Pacific).

Pale monocle bream, *Scolopsis affinis*, 28 cm (W. Pacific).

Two-lined monocle bream, *Scolopsis bilineatus*, 20 cm (mainly W. Pacific).

Two-lined monocle bream, *Scolopsis bilineatus*, juvenile, 5 cm (mainly W. Pacific).

Bridled monocle bream, *Scolopsis frenatus*, 10 cm (W. Indian Ocean).

Pearly monocle bream, *Scolopsis margaritifer*, 25 cm (W. Pacific).

Monogrammed monocle bream, *Scolopsis monogramma*, 28 cm (W. Pacific).

Whitecheek monocle bream, *Scolopsis vosmeri*, 20 cm.

Yellowstripe goatfish, *Mulloides flavolineatus*, 30 cm.

Yellowfin goatfish, *Mulloides vanicolensis*, 30 cm.

Bicolor goatfish, *Parupeneus barberinoides*, 22 cm (W. Pacific).

Dash-dot goatfish, *Parupeneus barberinus*, 38 cm.

Doublebar goatfish, *Parupeneus bifasciatus*, 28 cm.

Goldsaddle goatfish, *Parupeneus cyclostomus*, yellow variety, 25 cm.

Goldsaddle goatfish, *Parupeneus cyclostomus*, dark variety, 30 cm.

Manybar goatfish, *Parupeneus multifasciatus*, 28 cm (W. Pacific).

Golden sweeper, *Parapriacanthus ransonneti* (Pempheridae), 6 cm.

Vanicolo sweeper, *Pempheris vanicolensis* (Pempheridae), 15 cm.

Topsail drummer, *Kyphosus cinerascens* (Kyphosidae), 30 cm.

Long-finned drummer, *Kyphosus vaigiensis* (Kyphosidae), 30 cm.

Stripey, *Microcanthus strigatus* (Kyphosidae), 12 cm (W. Pacific).

Orbicular batfish, *Platax orbicularis*, 30 cm.

Pinnate batfish, *Platax pinnatus*, 40 cm (W. Pacific).

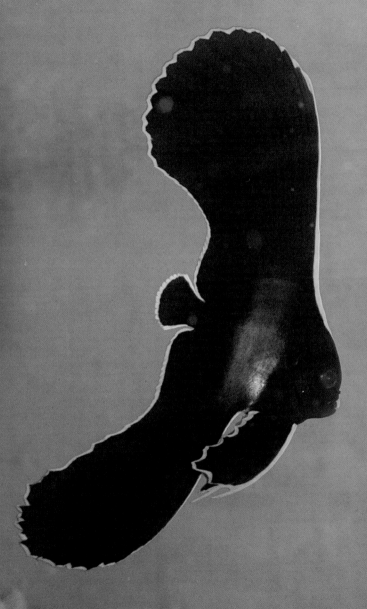

Pinnate batfish, *Platax pinnatus*, juvenile, 8 cm (W. Pacific).

Teira batfish, *Platax teira*, 45 cm.

Teira batfish, *Platax teira*, juveniles, 12 cm.

Threadfin butterflyfish, *Chaetodon auriga*, 20 cm.

Oriental butterflyfish, *Chaetodon auripes*, 15 cm (Japan and Taiwan).

Exquisite butterflyfish, *Chaetodon austriacus*, 12 cm (Red Sea).

Triangular butterflyfish, *Chaetodon baronessa*, 13 cm (W. Pacific (*C. triangulum* from Indian Ocean is similar).

Bennett's butterflyfish, *Chaetodon bennetti*, 12 cm.

Speckled butterflyfish, *Chaetodon citrinellus*, 10 cm.

Collare butterflyfish, *Chaetodon collare*, 14 cm (mainly Indian Ocean).

Indian Vagabond butterflyfish, *Chaetodon decussatus*, 18 cm (Indian Ocean).

Saddled butterflyfish, *Chaetodon ephippium*, 18 cm.

Saddleback butterflyfish, *Chaetodon falcula*, 16 cm (Indian Ocean)

Red Sea Racoon butterflyfish, *Chaetodon fasciatus*, 22 cm (Red Sea).

Bluestripe butterflyfish, *Chaetodon fremblii*, 12 cm (Hawaiian Islands) (J. Randall).

Spotted butterflyfish, *Chaetodon guttatissimus*, 12 cm (Indian Ocean).

Klein's butterflyfish, *Chaetodon kleinii*, 12 cm.

Orange-face butterflyfish, *Chaetodon larvatus*, 12 cm (Red Sea).

Somali butterflyfish, *Chaetodon leucopleura*, 15 cm (W. Indian Ocean).

Lined butterflyfish, *Chaetodon lineolatus*, 25 cm.

Racoon butterflyfish, *Chaetodon lunula*, 18 cm.

Blackback butterflyfish, *Chaetodon melannotus*, 12 cm.

Arabian butterflyfish, *Chaetodon melapterus*, 10 cm.

Merten's butterflyfish, *Chaetodon mertensii*, 10 cm.

Whiteface butterflyfish, *Chaetodon mesoleucos*, 13 cm (Red Sea) (J. Randall).

Meyer's butterflyfish, *Chaetodon meyeri*, 15 cm.

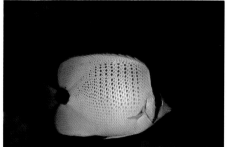

Lemon butterflyfish, *Chaetodon miliaris*, 10 cm (Hawaiian Islands) (J. Randall).

Multiband butterflyfish, *Chaetodon multicinctus*, 10 cm (Hawaiian Islands) (J. Randall).

Black-spotted butterflyfish, *Chaetodon nigropunctatus*, 10 cm (Persian Gulf to E. Africa).

Japanese butterflyfish, *Chaetodon nippon*, 10 cm (Japan).

Eight-banded butterflyfish, *Chaetodon octofasciatus*, 8cm (mainly W. Pacific).

Ornate butterflyfish, *Chaetodon ornatus*, 14 cm.

Redback butterflyfish, *Chaetodon paucifasciatus*, 12 cm (Red Sea).

Bluespot butterflyfish, *Chaetodon plebius*, 10 cm.

Spot-banded butterflyfish, *Chaetodon punctatofasciatus*, 10 cm (mainly W. Pacific).

Fourspot butterflyfish, *Chaetodon quadrimaculatus*, 12 cm (W. Pacific).

Latticed butterflyfish, *Chaetodon rafflesi*, 14 cm.

Reticulated butterflyfish, *Chaetodon reticulatus*, 14 cm (W. Pacific).

Golden butterflyfish, *Chaetodon semilarvatus*, 15 cm (Red Sea).

Dotted butterflyfish, *Chaetodon semion*, 18 cm.

Ovalspot butterflyfish, *Chaetodon speculum*, 12 cm (mainly W. Pacific).

Chevroned butterflyfish, *Chaetodon trifascialis*, 15 cm.

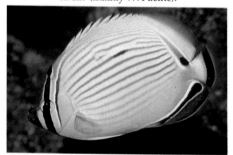

Redfin butterflyfish, *Chaetodon trifasciatus*, 13 cm.

Pacific Double-saddle butterflyfish, *Chaetodon ulietensis*, 14 cm (W. Pacific).

Teardrop butterflyfish, *Chaetodon unimaculatus*, 15 cm.

Vagabond butterflyfish, *Chaetodon vagabundus*, 14 cm.

Yellowhead butterflyfish, *Chaetodon xanthocephalus*, 18 cm (W. Indian Ocean).

Beaked coralfish, *Chelmon rostratus*, 15 cm (mainly W. Pacific).

Orange-banded coralfish, *Coradion chrysozonus*, 10 cm (W. Pacific).

Longnose butterflyfish, *Forcipiger flavissimus*, 15 cm (*F. longirostris* is nearly identical, but snout longer).

Pyramid butterflyfish, *Hemitaurichthys polylepis*, 18 cm (W. Pacific).

Black Pyramid butterflyfish, *Hemitaurichthys zoster*, 16 cm (W. Indian Ocean).

Longfin bannerfish, *Heniochus acuminatus*, 22 cm.

Pennant bannerfish, *Heniochus chrysostomus*, 12 cm (mainly W. Pacific).

Red Sea bannerfish, *Heniochus intermedius*, 18 cm (Red Sea).

Masked bannerfish, *Heniochus monoceros*, 22 cm.

Indian bannerfish, *Heniochus pleurotaenia*, 15 cm (Sumatra to Sri Lanka).

Singular bannerfish, *Heniochus singularius*, 20 cm (mainly W. Pacific)

Humphead bannerfish, *Heniochus varius*, 16 cm (W. Pacific).

Ocellated coralfish, *Parachaetodon ocellatus*, 10 cm (W. Pacific).

Threespot angelfish, *Apolemichthys trimaculatus*, 18 cm.

Bicolor angelfish, *Centropyge bicolor*, 12 cm (mainly W. Pacific).

Two-spined angelfish, *Centropyge bispinosus*, 8 cm.

Eibl's angelfish, *Centropyge eibli*, 10 cm (E. and C. Indian Ocean).

Lemonpeel angelfish, *Centropyge flavissimus*, 12 cm (mainly W. Pacific).

Herald's angelfish, *Centropyge heraldi*, 10 cm (W. Pacific).

Flame angelfish, *Centropyge loriculus*, 8 cm (W. Pacific).

Potter's angelfish, *Centropyge potteri*, 8 cm (Hawaiian Islands).

Pearl-scaled angelfish, *Centropyge vroliki*, 8 cm (mainly W. Pacific).

Keyhole angelfish, *Centropyge tibicen*, 12 cm (mainly W. Pacific).

Vermiculated angelfish, *Chaetodontoplus mesoleucus*, 14 cm (W. Pacific).

Bandit angelfish, *Desmoholacanthus arcuatus*, 10 cm (Hawaiian Islands) (J. Randall).

Zebra angelfish, *Genicanthus caudovittatus*, male, 15 cm (Red Sea).

Zebra angelfish, *Genicanthus caudovittatus*, female, 12 cm (Red Sea).

Blackspot angelfish, *Genicanthus melanospilos*, male, 15 cm (W. Pacific).

Blackspot angelfish, *Genicanthus melanospilos*, female, 15 cm (W. Pacific).

Blue-ringed angelfish, *Pomacanthus annularis*, 30 cm.

Arabian angelfish, *Pomacanthus asfur*, 30 cm (Red Sea).

Earspot angelfish, *Pomacanthus chrysurus*, 24 cm (W. Indian Ocean).

Emperor angelfish, *Pomacanthus imperator*, 35 cm.

African pygmy angelfish, *Centropyge acanthops*, 6 cm (W. Indian Ocean).

Yellowband angelfish, *Pomacanthus maculosus*, 30 cm. (Persian Gulf, Red Sea, and NW Indian Ocean).

Blue-girdled angelfish, *Pomacanthus navarchus*, 28 cm (W. Pacific).

Semicircle angelfish, *Pomacanthus semicirculatus*, 30 cm.

Six-banded angelfish, *Pomacanthus sexstriatus*, 40 cm (W. Pacific).

Yellowmask angelfish, *Pomacanthus xanthometopon*, 35 cm (W. Pacific).

Regal angelfish, *Pygoplites diacanthus*, 23 cm.

Maomao, *Abudefduf abdominalis*, 15 cm (Hawaiian Islands).

Bengal sergeant, *Abudefduf bengalensis*, 12 cm.

Scissortail sergeant, *Abudefduf sexfasciatus*, 12 cm.

Blackspot sergeant, *Abudefduf sordidus*, 15 cm.

Indo-Pacific sergeant, *Abudefduf vaigiensis*, 14 cm.

Golden damsel, *Amblyglyphidodon aureus*, 10 cm.

Staghorn damsel, *Amblyglyphidodon curacao*, 8 cm (W. Pacific).

Whitebelly damsel, *Amblyglyphidodon leucogaster*, 8 cm.

Skunk anemonefish, *Amphiprion akallopisos*, 8 cm
(Indian Ocean).

Barrier Reef anemonefish, *Amphiprion akindynos*,
10 cm (Great Barrier Reef and Coral Sea).

Allard's anemonefish, *Amphiprion allardi*, 10 cm
(E. Africa).

Twoband anemonefish, *Amphiprion bicinctus*,
10 cm (Red Sea).

Mauritian anemonefish, *Amphiprion chrysogaster*,
12 cm (Mauritius).

Orange-fin anemonefish, *Amphiprion chrysopterus*,
10 cm (W. Pacific)

Clark's anemonefish, *Amphiprion clarkii*, 10 cm.

Clark's anemonefish, *Amphiprion clarkii*, 10 cm.

Red saddleback anemonefish, *Amphiprion ephippium*, 8 cm (Andaman Sea to Java).

Seychelles anemonefish, *Amphiprion fuscocaudatus*, 12 cm (Seychelles and Aldabra).

Tomato anemonefish, *Amphiprion frenatus*, 8 cm (Japan to Indonesia).

Whitebonnet anemonefish, *Amphiprion leucokranos*, 8 cm (New Guinea and Solomon Islands)

Red and black anemonefish, *Amphiprion melanopus*, 8 cm (W. Pacific).

Maldives anemonefish, *Amphiprion nigripes*, 8 cm (Maldive Islands and Sri Lanka).

False Clown anemonefish, *Amphiprion ocellaris*, 8 cm (W. Pacific).

Clown anemonefish, *Amphiprion percula*, 7 cm (NE Australia and Melanesia).

Spinecheek anemonefish, *Premnas biaculeatus*, 12 cm (W. Pacific).

Pink anemonefish, *Amphiprion perideraion*, 8 cm (mainly W. Pacific).

Saddleback anemonefish, *Amphiprion polymnus*, 10 cm (W. Pacific).

Orange anemonefish, *Amphiprion sandaracinos*, 8 cm (W. Pacific).

Sebae anemonefish, *Amphiprion sebae*, 10 cm (Indian Ocean).

Twotone chromis, *Chromis dimidiata*, 5 cm
(Indian Ocean).

Scaly chromis, *Chromis lepidolepis*, 5 cm.

Bicolor chromis, *Chromis margaritifer*, 5 cm
(mainly W. Pacific).

Hawaiian chromis, *Chromis ovalis*, 10 cm
(Hawaiian Islands).

Blackbar chromis, *Chromis retrofasciata*, 4 cm
(W. Pacific).

Ternate chromis, *Chromis ternatensis*, 6 cm.

Blue-green chromis, *Chromis viridis*, 6 cm.

Paletail chromis, *Chromis xanthura*, 10 cm
(W. Pacific).

Damselfishes – Family Pomacentridae

Twospot demoiselle, *Chrysiptera biocellata*, 8 cm.

Blue Devil, *Chrysiptera cyanea*, male, 8 cm (W. Pacific). (female has bluish tail & black spot on dorsal fin)

Surge demoiselle, *Chrysiptera leucopma* 5 cm.

Goldtail demoiselle, *Chrysiptera parasema*, 4 cm (W. Pacific).

Rolland's demoiselle, *Chrysiptera rollandi*, 4 cm (mainly W. Pacific).

Talbot's demoiselle, *Chrysiptera talboti*, 4 cm (W. Pacific)

Onespot demoiselle, *Chrysiptera unimaculata*, 6 cm.

Springer's demoiselle, *Chrysiptera springeri*, 5 cm (W. Pacific).

Reticulated Dascyllus, *Dascyllus reticulatus*, 5 cm (mainly W. Pacific).

Hawaiian Dascyllus, *Dascyllus albisella*, 8 cm (Hawaiian Islands).

Humbug Dascyllus, *Dascyllus aruanus*, 4 cm (*D. melanurus* of W. Pacific is similar, but has black tail fin).

Threespot Dascyllus, *Dascyllus trimaculatus*, 6 cm.

Blackvent damsel, *Dischistodus melanotus*, 10 cm (W. Pacific).

Black damsel, *Neoglyphidodon melas*, juvenile, 5 cm (adult is solid black).

Behn's damsel, *Neoglyphidodon nigroris*, 8 cm (W. Pacific).

Behn's damsel, *Neoglyphidodon nigroris*, juvenile, 3 cm (W. Pacific).

Javanese damsel, *Neoglyphidodon oxyodon*, juvenile, 4 cm (Indonesia & Philippines).

Yellowtail demoiselle, *Neopomacentrus azysron*, 5 cm

Dick's damsel, *Plectroglyphidodon dickii*, 6 cm.

Johnston damsel, *Plectroglyphidodon johnstonianus*, 6 cm.

Jewel damsel, *Plectroglyphidodon lacrymatus*, 7 cm.

Blue damsel, *Pomacentrus pavo*, 7 cm.

Caerulean damsel, *Pomacentrus caeruleus*, 5 cm
(W. Indian Ocean)

Neon damsel, *Pomacentrus coelestis*, 5 cm
(W. Pacific & E. Indian Ocean).

Lemon damsel, *Pomacentrus moluccensis*, 5 cm
(mainly W. Pacific)

Goldback damsel, *Pomacentrus nigromanus*, 6 cm
(W. Pacific).

Princess damsel, *Pomacentrus vaiuli*, 6 cm (mainly W. Pacific).

Sulphur damsel, *Pomacentrus sulfureus*, 7 cm
(Red Sea & W. Indian Ocean).

Threeline damsel, *Pomacentrus trilineatus*, 6 cm
(Red Sea & W. Indian Ocean)

Pacific gregory, *Stegastes fasciolatus*, 10 cm.

Dusky gregory, *Stegastes nigricans*, 10 cm (broad
white bar evident during courtship & nesting).

Dwarf hawkfish, *Cirrhitichthys falco*, 6 cm (W. Pacific & E. Indian Ocean).

Threadfin hawkfish, *Cirrhitichthys aprinus*, 8 cm (W. Pacific).

Pixy hawkfish, *Cirrhitichthys oxycephalus*, 6 cm.

Stocky hawkfish, *Cirrhitus pinnulatus*, 18 cm.

Swallowtail hawkfish, *Cyprinocirrhites polyactis*, 10 cm.

Longnose hawkfish, *Oxycirrhites typus*, 8 cm.

Flame hawkfish, *Neocirrhites armatus*, 6 cm
(W. Pacific).

Arceye hawkfish, *Paracirrhites arcatus*, 10 cm.

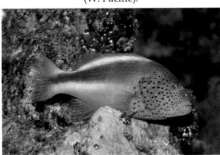

Blackside hawkfish, *Paracirrhites forsteri*, 15 cm.

Halfspotted hawkfish, *Paracirrhites hemistictus*,
22 cm (mainly W. Pacific).

Chevron barracuda, *Sphyraena qenie*, 100 cm.

Great barracuda, *Sphyraena barracuda*, 70 cm.

Bluespotted wrasse, *Anampses caeruleopunctatus*, female, 12 cm.

Pearl wrasse, *Anampses cuvier*, 14 cm (Hawaiian Islands) (J. Randall).

Spotted wrasse, *Anampses meleagrides*, male, 20 cm.

Spotted wrasse, *Anampses meleagrides*, female, 14 cm.

Axilspot hogfish, *Bodianus axillaris*, 18 cm.

Saddleback hogfish, *Bodianus bilunulatus*, 28 cm.

Diana's hogfish, *Bodianus diana*, 20 cm.

Blackfin hogfish, *Bodianus loxozonus*, 30 cm. (W. Pacific)

Splitfin hogfish, *Bodianus mesothorax*, 18 cm (W. Pacific).

Twospot wrasse, *Cheilinus bimaculatus*, 10 cm.

Redbreasted wrasse, *Cheilinus fasciatus*, 28 cm.

Red Sea wrasse, *Cheilinus lunulatus*, 70 cm (Red Sea).

Tripletail wrasse, *Cheilinus trilobatus*, 35 cm.

Humphead or Giant wrasse, *Cheilinus undulatus*, 190 cm.

Cigar wrasse, *Cheilio inermis*, 38 cm.

Anchor tuskfish, *Choerodon anchorago*, 35 cm (W. Pacific & E. Indian Ocean).

Harlequin tuskfish, *Choerodon fasciatus*, 25 cm (W. Pacific).

Blueside wrasse, *Cirrhilabrus cyanopleura*, 12 cm (W. Pacific).

Exquisite wrasse, *Cirrhilabrus exquisitus*, 10 cm.

Clown coris, *Coris aygula*, 14 cm.

Clown coris, *Coris aygula*, juvenile, 4 cm.

Yellowtail coris, *Coris gaimard*, 22 cm.

Yellowtail coris, *Coris gaimard*, juvenile, 4 cm.

Slingjaw wrasse, *Epibulus insidiator*, 25 cm.

Bird wrasse, *Gomphosus varius*, 18 cm (W. Pacific; *G. caeruleus* of the Indian Ocean is similar)

Checkerboard wrasse, *Halichoeres hortulanus*, 24 cm.

Tailspot wrasse, *Halichoeres melanurus*, 8 cm (W. Pacific).

Ornate wrasse, *Halichoeres ornatissimus*, 12 cm (W. Pacific)

Zigzag wrasse, *Halichoeres scapularis*, 18 cm.

Threespot wrasse, *Halichoeres trimaculatus*, 12 cm (mainly W. Pacific)

Barred thicklip, *Hemigymnus fasciatus*, 30 cm.

Blackeye thicklip, *Hemigymnus melapterus*, 30 cm.

Pastel ringwrasse, *Hologymnosus doliatus*, 30 cm.

Tubelip wrasse, *Labrichthys unilineatus*, 12 cm.

Bicolor cleaner wrasse, *Labroides bicolor*, 10 cm.

Cleaner wrasse, *Labroides dimidiatus*, 8 cm.

Ornate wrasse, *Macropharyngodon ornatus*, 10 cm..

Rockmover wrasse, *Novaculichthys taeniourus*, 25 cm.

Eightstripe wrasse, *Pseudocheilinus octotaenia*, 11 cm.

Bluelined wrasse, *Stethojulis bandanensis*, 8 cm (W. Pacific).

Stripebelly wrasse, *Stethojulis strigiventer*, 8 cm.

Bluntheaded wrasse, *Thalassoma amblycephalum*, male, 14 cm.

Bluntheaded wrasse, *Thalassoma amblycephalum*, female, 7cm.

Sixbar wrasse, *Thalassoma hardwicke*, 14 cm.

Hebrew wrasse, *Thalassoma hebraicum*, 25 cm (W. Indian Ocean).

Jansen's wrasse, *Thalassoma jansenii*, 14 cm.

Moon wrasse, *Thalassoma lunare*, 20 cm.

Sunset wrasse, *Thalassoma lutescens*, 20 cm (mainly W. Pacific).

Klunzinger's wrasse, *Thalassoma klunzingeri*, 14 cm (Red Sea).

Pavo razorfish, *Xyrichtys pavo*, 10 cm.

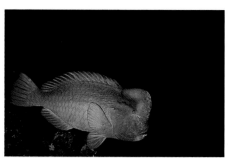

Bumphead parrotfish, *Bolbometopon muricatum*, 100 cm.

Bicolor parrotfish, *Cetoscarus bicolor*, 70 cm.

Bicolor parrotfish, *Cetoscarus bicolor*, juvenile, 8 cm.

Bleeker's parrotfish, *Scarus bleekeri*, 35 cm (W. Pacific).

Bridled parrotfish, *Scarus frenatus*, 30 cm.

Bluebarred parrotfish, *Scarus ghobban*, 38 cm.

Egghead parrotfish, *Scarus oviceps*, 28 cm (W. Pacific; *S. scaber* of the Indian Ocean is similar)

Dusky parrotfish, *Scarus prasiognathus*, 50 cm.

Yellowfin parrotfish, *Scarus flavipectoralis*, 30 cm (W. Pacific).

Swarthy parrotfish, *Scarus niger*, 30 cm.

Ember parrotfish, *Scarus rubroviolaceus*, male, 60 cm.

Ember parrotfish, *Scarus rubroviolaceus*, female, 35 cm.

Schlegel's parrotfish, *Scarus schlegeli*, female, 28 cm (W. Pacific).

Schlegel's parrotfish, *Scarus schlegeli*, male, 35 cm (W. Pacific).

Bullethead parrotfish, *Scarus sordidus*, 30 cm.

Indian steephead parrotfish, *Scarus strongycephalus*, 60 cm (Indian Ocean).

Indonesian jawfish, *Opistognathus* sp.
(Opistognathidae), 10 cm (W. Pacific).

Spotted sand-diver, *Trichonotus setiger*
(Trichonotidae), 12 cm.

Sharpnose sandperch, *Parapercis cylindrica*
(Pinguipedidae), 10 cm (W. Pacific)

Speckled sandperch, *Parapercis hexophthalma*
(Pinguipedidae), 18 cm.

Neon triplefin, *Helcogramma striata*
(Tripterygiidae), 3 cm (W. Pacific).

Bigmouth triplefin, *Helcogramma* sp.
(Tripterygiidae), 5 cm.

Earspot Blenny, *Cirripectes auritus*
(Blenniidae), 9 cm.

Chesnut blenny, *Cirripectes castaneus*
(Blenniidae), 8 cm.

Lined blenny, *Ecsenius lineatus*, 5 cm (W. Pacific & E. Indian Ocean).

Bicolor blenny, *Ecsenius bicolor*, 6 cm
(W. Pacific & E. Indian Ocean).

Midas blenny, *Ecsenius midas*, 8 cm.

Leopard blenny, *Exallias brevis*, 10 cm.

Dussumier's rockskipper, *Istiblennius dussumieri*,
10 cm.

Striped fangblenny, *Meiacanthus grammistes*, 10 cm (W. Pacific).

Blue-streaked rockskipper, *Istiblennius periophthalmus*, 10 cm.

Yellowtail fangblenny, *Meiacanthus atrodorsalis*, 8 cm (W. Pacific).

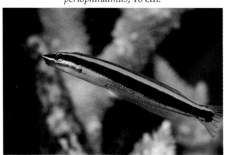

Blue-lined fangblenny, *Plagiotremus rhinorhynchos*, 8 cm (is also a largely orange variety)

Banded blenny, *Salarias fasciatus*, 12 cm.

Marbled dragonet, *Synchiropus marmoratus* (Callionymidae), 4 cm (W. Indian Ocean).

Mandarinfish, *Synchiropus splendidus*
(Callionymidae), 5 cm (W. Pacific)

Starry dragonet, *Synchiropus stellatus*
(Callionymidae), 4 cm.

Banded shrimp goby, *Amblyeleotris fasciata*
(Gobiidae), 6 cm.

Steinitz' shrimp goby, *Amblyeleotris steinitzi*
(Gobiidae), 6 cm.

Orange-striped goby, *Amblygobius decussatus*, 8 cm (W. Pacific).

Banded goby, *Amblygobius phalaena*, 12 cm.

Hector's goby, *Amblygobius hectori*, 5 cm.

Yellow shrimp goby, *Cryptocentrus cinctus*, 6 cm (W. Pacific).

Doublebar goby, *Eviota bifasciata*, 3 cm (W. Pacific).

Silver-lined mudskipper, *Periophthalmus argentilineatus*, 10 cm.

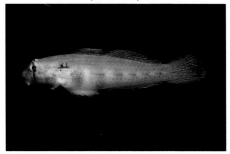

Shoulderspot goby, *Fusigobius scapulostigma*, 5 cm (W. Pacific & E. Indian Ocean)

Fourbar goby, *Gobiodon citrinus*, 2 cm.

Coral goby, *Pleurosicya mossambica*, 2 cm.

Decorated goby, *Istigobius decoratus*, 10 cm.

Twinspot goby, *Signigobius biocellatus*,
5 cm (W. Pacific).

Twostripe goby, *Valenciennea helsdingenii*, 14 cm.

Long-finned goby, *Valenciennea longipinnis*, 14 cm.

Orange-dashed goby, *Valenciennea puellaris*, 12 cm.

Blueband goby, *Valenciennea strigata*, 15 cm.

Fire dartfish, *Nemateleotris magnifica*, 7 cm.

Elegant firefish, *Nemateleotris decora*, 7 cm.

Twotone dartfish, *Ptereleotris evides*, 12 cm.

Spot-tail dartfish, *Ptereleotris heteroptera*, 10 cm.

Curious wormfish, *Gunnellichthys curiosus*, 12 cm.

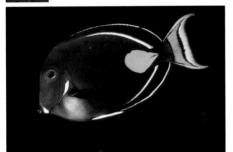

Achilles tang, *Acanthurus achilles*,
20 cm (Pacific).

Eyestripe surgeonfish, *Acanthurus dussumieri*,
35 cm.

Whitecheek surgeonfish, *Acanthurus nigricans*,
20 cm.

Striped surgeonfish, *Acanthurus lineatus*, 35 cm.

Elongate surgeonfish, *Acanthurus mata*, 50 cm.

Blackstreak surgeonfish, *Acanthurus nigricauda*,
30 cm.

Orangeband surgeonfish, *Acanthurus olivaceus*,
30 cm (W. Pacific)

Mimic surgeonfish, *Acanthurus pyroferus*,
25 cm (W. Pacific).

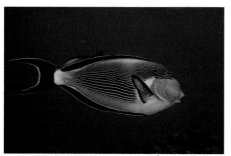

Sohal surgeonfish, *Acanthurus sohal*,
30 cm (Red Sea).

Convict surgeonfish, *Acanthurus triostegus*, 25 cm.

Yellowfin surgeonfish, *Acanthurus xanthopterus*,
38 cm.

Lined bristletooth, *Ctenochaetus striatus*, 22 cm.

Spotted unicornfish, *Naso brevirostris*, 38 cm.

Orangespine unicornfish, *Naso lituratus*, 35 cm.

Humpnose unicornfish, *Naso tuberosus*, 50 cm.

Bluespine unicornfish, *Naso unicornis*, 40 cm.

Vlaming's unicornfish, *Naso vlamingii*, 45 cm.

Palette surgeonfish, *Paracanthurus hepatus*, 12 cm.

Yellow tang, *Zebrasoma flavescens*, 13 cm (Hawaii & scattered localities in W. Pacific).

Sailfin tang, *Zebrasoma desjardinii*, 20 cm (Red Sea & W. Indian Ocean; *Z. veliferum* from Pacific is similar).

Brushtail tang, *Zebrasoma scopas*, 16 cm.

Yellowtail surgeonfish, *Zebrasoma xanthurum*, 20 cm (Red Sea & Persian Gulf).

Moorish idol, *Zanclus cornutus*, (Zanclidae) 22 cm.

Forktail rabbitfish, *Siganus argenteus*, 20 cm.

Coral rabbitfish, *Siganus corallinus*, 28 cm.

Barred rabbitfish, *Siganus doliatus*, 20 cm (W. Pacific;
S. virgatus of W. Pacific-E. Indian Ocean is similar).

Spotted rabbitfish, *Siganus guttatus*, 30 cm
(W. Pacific).

Indian rabbitfish, *Siganus luridus*, 20 cm
(W. Indian Ocean).

Lemon rabbitfish, *Siganus puelloides*, 22 cm
(Maldives & Andaman Sea).

Starry rabbitfish, *Siganus stellatus*, 30 cm (Indian
Ocean; *S. punctatus* of W. Pacific is similar).

Foxface, *Siganus vulpinus*, 25 cm (W. Pacific).

Flowery flounder, *Bothus mancus*, 30 cm.

Panther flounder, *Bothus pantherinus*, 8 cm.

Orange-lined triggerfish, *Balistapus undulatus*, 22 cm.

Clown triggerfish, *Balistoides conspicillum*, 12 cm.

Redtooth triggerfish, *Odonus niger*, 30 cm.

Titan triggerfish, *Balistoides viridescens*, 50 cm.

Indian triggerfish, *Melichthys indicus*, 28 cm (Indian Ocean; *M. niger*, a circumtropical species is similar).

Pinktail triggerfish, *Melichthys vidua*, 26 cm.

White-barred triggerfish, *Rhinecanthus aculeatus*, 20 cm.

Blackpatch triggerfish, *Rhinecanthus verrucosus*, 20 cm (W. Pacific).

Picasso triggerfish, *Rhinecanthus assasi*,
20 cm (Red Sea).

Wedge-tail triggerfish, *Rhinecanthus rectangulus*, 20 cm.

Pallid triggerfish, *Sufflamen bursa*, 20 cm.

Flagtail triggerfish, *Sufflamen chrysopterus*, 20 cm.

Scrawled filefish, *Alutera scripta*, 40 cm.

Brush-sided filefish, *Amanses scopas*, 18 cm.

Yelloweye filefish, *Cantherhines dumerilii*, 28 cm.

Honeycomb filefish, *Cantherhines pardalis*, 15 cm.

Beaked or Longnose filefish, *Oxymonacanthus longirostris*, 8 cm.

Mimic filefish, *Paraluteres prionurus*, 8 cm.

Orangetail filefish, *Pervagor aspricaudus*, 10 cm.

Hawaiian filefish, *Pervagor spilosoma*, 10 cm (Hawaiian Islands) (J. Randall).

Thornback cowfish, *Lactoria fornasini*, 8 cm.

Longhorn cowfish, *Lactoria cornuta*, 18 cm.

Yellow boxfish, *Ostracion cubicus*, 18 cm.

Spotted boxfish, *Ostracion meleagris*, male, 13 cm.

Spotted boxfish, *Ostracion meleagris*, female, 10 cm.

Star puffer, *Arothron stellatus*, 40 cm.

Bristly puffer, *Arothron hispidus*, 25 cm.

Striped puffer, *Arothron manilensis*, 25 cm.

Guineafowl puffer, *Arothron meleagris*, 30 cm.

Black-spotted puffer, *Arothron nigropunctatus*, 30 cm.

347

Three-barred sharpnose puffer, *Canthigaster coronata*, 10 cm.

Bennett's sharpnose puffer, *Canthigaster bennetti*, 5 cm.

Solander's sharpnose puffer, *Canthigaster solandri*, 10 cm.

Black-saddled sharpnose puffer, *Canthigaster valentini*, 8 cm.

Freckled porcupinefish, *Diodon holocanthus*, 22 cm (Diodontidae).

Spotted porcupinefish, *Diodon hystrix*, 35 cm.

Black-blotched porcupinefish, *Diodon liturosus*, 35 cm.

Chapter 22

Sea Snakes
Friend or Foe ?

Sea snakes are highly venomous, but usually are no cause for alarm. At one stage we were absolutely convinced these reptiles were completely inoffensive. However, this notion was dispelled following an incident at Ashmore Reef, off Australia's northwestern coast. We were transferring a 44-gallon drum of fuel from the shore to our vessel over a distance of about 100 meters. The drum, which floated, was secured with a rope line and pulled hand over hand out to the boat. This operation attracted the attention of a passing sea snake, which dramatically veered off course to intercept the drum. It quickly overtook the bobbing target. We were absolutely amazed at the scene that unfolded. The snake repeatedly tried to bite the drum. There was no doubt about its intentions. It was greatly agitated and continued to strike at the drum as we hoisted it on deck. So much for the placid temperament theory!

In actual fact, sea snakes are seldom encounterd by divers or reef walkers at most locations. Only the two similar appearing Sea Kraits of the genus *Laticauda* are seen regularly, mainly on reefs of the western and central Pacific. There are approximately 50 species of sea snakes, nearly all belonging to the family Hydrophidae. They range throughout the tropical Indo-Pacific region, but by far the majority of species live close to continental coasts from the Persian Gulf to the Indonesian Archipelago and Australia. The Pelagic sea snake *(Pelamis platurus)* is the most widespread species, ranging from East Africa to the Pacific coast of the Americas. It lives in the open sea, sometimes hundreds of kilometers from the nearest land. Tiny Ashmore Reef must surely rate as the world's sea snake capital. Twelve species have been recorded. A reef walk through shallow water at Ashmore is like negotiating a mine field. Well camouflaged and coiled, snakes are everywhere!

Deadly poisonous

Most sea snakes are relatively helpless and unable to strike on land. But they definitely should not be handled. The venom is highly potent. Perhaps the most poisonous is the Beaked sea snake, which ranges from the Seychelles to the Coral Sea. An average sized snake can produce 10-15 milligrams of venom. A fatal dose of venom for an adult human is only 1.5 milligrams! On the bright side, we have never heard of a fatal attack on a diver, snorkeler, or wader. But fatalities are recorded regularly in southeast Asia. The victims are mainly fishermen that are careless in removing entangled snakes from nets.

Sea snakes feed mainly on fishes, particularly small bottom living varieties. The banded sea kraits are active hunters during the day and can be seen probing crevices and holes. Stomach contents indicate they feed largely on small gobies that live in burrows. Like their terrestrial counterparts, sea snakes are air breathers, and therefore must periodically return to the surface. There is little accurate information regarding their ability to stay submerged. We have watched individuals remain underwater for 10 minutes or so and experts estimate that some

◄ A Banded sea krait heads for the bottom after gulping air at the surface.

species may remain submerged for several hours. We have seen sea kraits at depths to about 40 meters, but judging from the types of fishes found in the stomachs it seems that most snakes frequent depths between 5 and 10 meters.

How to tell an eel from a sea snake

Eels, especially certain types of snake eels (family Ophichthidae), are frequently confused with sea snakes. One species in particular, the Harlequin snake eel (*Myrichthys colubrinus*) has a color pattern remarkably similar to that of the sea kraits. However, at close inspection it is easy to tell these animals apart. Sea snakes are differentiated by their distinctive scales and paddle-shaped tail. Eels lack scales, frequently have a long-based fin along the back and lower edge of the body, and have a gill opening behind the head. The largest sea snakes grow to slightly over two meters, but most that are seen are only about half this size.

Leaf-scaled sea snake,
Aipysurus foliosquama, 150 cm.

Olive or Golden sea snake,
Aipysurus laevis, 150 cm.

Poole's sea snake, *Aipysurus pooleorum*, 120 cm.

Beaked sea snake, *Enhydrina schistosa* 120 cm.

Turtlehead sea snake,
Emydocephalus annulatus, 120 cm.

Stokes' sea snake, *Astrotia stokesii*, 100 cm.

Chinese sea snake, *Laticauda semifasciata*, 100 cm.

Banded sea snake, *Laticauda colubrina* 120 cm.

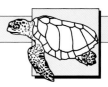

Chapter 23

Turtles
The Ancient Mariners

The turtles we see swimming over the reef are very similar to ancestral forms that shared the seas with ichthyosaurs and pleiosaurs 150 million years ago! Obviously these "survivors" are extremely well adapted for life in the oceanic realm. Unfortunately, their continued existence is increasingly threatened. In many areas turtle meat and eggs are utilized for food, the oils are used in the cosmetic industry and for medication, and the shells are shaped into bits of jewelry. As a result humans are their biggest threat. Moreover, many turtles are accidentally killed each year by drowning in trawl nets or become entangled in set nets. They also fall victim to bits of plastic debris, which if mistaken for food can fatally block the breathing and digestive passages. Large, fully grown turtles have few natural enemies. Occasionally they are attacked by sharks and killer whales.

Only six species

Six of the eight species of marine turtles are found in the vast Indo-Pacific region. Although somewhat diverse in appearance and habits they share certain similarities. All are fully aquatic except for brief periods when the female comes ashore to deposit her eggs. Most migrate over long distances to reach favored breeding sites, in some case the same beach or island where they were hatched. Breeding occurs in cycles that vary from about 1-5 years, but on average a female will breed about once every two years. Nesting frequently takes place during summer or autumn and a single female

usually lays several batches of eggs at 2-3 week intervals. A hole is excavated with the hind flippers and about 50-150 eggs are deposited. They are immediately covered with a layer of sand. Incubation time is variable, but for most species lasts about two months.

Mortality of the eggs and hatchlings is extremely heavy. Besides man, nest robbers include ghost crabs, dogs, monitor lizards, foxes, and monkeys. Hatching usually occurs at night. After emerging from the nest the young turtles must literally run the gauntlet in their dash to the sea. They are extremely vulnerable to the above mentioned predators as well as various sea birds. Those lucky enough to reach the sea face an onslaught of sharks and large fishes from below and birds of prey from above. The life of a young turtle is not easy!

Most turtles are mainly carnivores that feed on a variety of swimming and bottom-living organisms. Such items as jellyfish, tunicates, sponges, soft corals, crabs, squids, and fishes are commonly consumed. Green turtles are initially carnivorous, but gradually shift to a vegetarian diet with increasing age. Adults feed on sea grasses and algae.

Today all species of turtles are considered threatened or endangered by the International Union for the Conservation of Nature and Natural Resources (IUCN). The Leatherback turtle in particular is thought to be especially vulnerable and populations have declined at an alarming rate.

◀ A Green sea turtle comes ashore to lay its eggs in the Coral Sea.

Loggerhead turtle, *Caretta caretta*, South Africa.

Turtle ride in the Coral Sea.

Green sea turtle, *Chelonia mydas*, Coral Sea.

Female Green sea turtle, *Chelonia mydas*, Coral Sea.

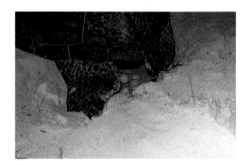

A Green sea turtle deposits its eggs, Coral Sea.

Green sea turtle, Indian Ocean.

Olive ridley turtle, *Lepidochelys olivacea*, Sulu Sea.

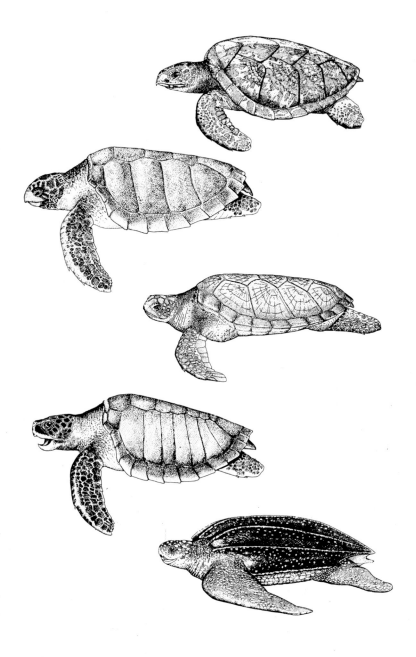

Marine turtles of the Indo-Pacific (courtesy of the Food and
Agricultural Organization of the United Nations).

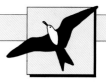

Sea Birds
Life and Death on a Coral Cay

If its your first visit to a coral reef chances are your attention will be riveted to the underwater scenery. There is such a wonderful diversity of life it is difficult to concentrate on anything else. But make the effort to do some bird watching if you have an opportunity. It is well worthwhile, particularly if there is a chance to visit a breeding colony.

The bird population of a tropical reef is dependent on several factors including the degree of isolation from human settlement, distance from continental shores, and the time of year. Coverage in this book is limited to a relatively few species that are commonly seen in the vicinity of reefs, sand cays and small islands. Excluded are waders (except the Reef heron) and various land birds that frequent the shores of continental areas or nearby islands.

A visit to a large seabird colony is an unforgettable experience. The raucous squawks and screeches are deafening and the air is filled with the heavy aroma of guano. It is possible to witness every aspect of the life cycle during a brief stroll. Adult birds are engaged in courtship and nesting activities, others are seen incubating their eggs. Parents alighting on the nest after a high seas feeding foray are greeted by a chorus of begging cries from their own chicks as well as those in adjacent nests. Chicks in all stages of development can often be observed. Dead chicks are also common. Many of them perish from malnutrition or are simply abandoned by their parents.

Reef heron

The Reef heron is often seen wading on reef flats at low tide. It feeds on various fishes, crustaceans, and other small invertebrates. Most individuals seen in the tropics are pure white in color, but there is also a gray variety. Herons lay 2-3 eggs on a platform of sticks that is lined with smaller twigs. They do not form colonies, but build isolated nests near the sea in trees or among rocks.

Terns

In contrast to the Reef heron, terns are gregarious birds that frequently form huge nesting colonies. They generally lay 1-3 eggs in simple nests located either on the ground or in the tops of bushes or low trees. Terns are very graceful fliers and efficient fish predators. They sight their prey from a considerable distance above the surface and make a sudden vertical plunge into the water. Small herrings (sardine-like fishes) are a favorite food item.

Boobies

Gannets or boobies are commonly encountered near reefs. The Brown booby is particularly abundant and frequents all tropical seas. They often nest at the same locality as terns. Most species lay a pair of eggs in a sandy depression near the beach, but the Red-footed booby nests in trees, often in association with frigate birds. Brown boobies sometimes follow boats at sea

---

◀ Male Greater frigate bird, *Fregata minor*, in full courtship display.

---

and may be remarkably tame. We have induced them to land on our head or outstretched hand by remaining very still on a prominent part of the boat, usually the bow or top of the wheel house.

Frigate birds

Frigate birds are among the most graceful of fliers. The skies above isolated cays and islands are sometimes filled with soaring frigates that reach amazing heights by gliding on updrafts. These elegant birds have a rather nasty disposition towards other sea birds. They obtain most of their food by thievery. Terns and boobies are dive bombed and generally harassed until they drop the fish they have just caught. The frigates then snatch the falling items in mid-air. They also snap up flying-fishes and surface floating food during low passes just above the water. Generally they do not alight at sea as they quickly become waterlogged. On land they are rather awkward and for this reason perch on branches that allow a full wing spread prior to take off. The distinctive throat pouch of the male frigate

becomes bright red and inflatable during the breeding season. This serves to attract the attention of potential mates. A single egg is laid in a nest built of sticks located on a bush or exposed rock.

Tropic birds

Tropic birds are somewhat similar to terns, but are more robust and have a characteristic flight pattern in which the wings are constantly flapped. At closer inspection they are easy to recognize on the basis of the two very elongate central tail feathers. Their breeding biology is slightly different than other sea birds. Usually they do not make a special nest, but take advantage of a preexisting sandy hollow or rocky depression. A single egg is laid and incubation by the parents is very intense. An incubating parent will not leave the nest if approached closely. The egg hatches in one month and it takes another two months before the young bird is fledged. It is actually deserted by the parents at this time and forced to fend for itself.

A tern colony on the Great Barrier Reef.

Red-footed booby and young Lesser frigate bird.

Lesser frigate bird (immature),
Fregata ariel (Fregatidae).

Reef heron, *Egretta sacra* (Ardeidae).

Sooty tern, *Sterna fuscata* (Laridae).

Common noddy tern, *Anous stolidus* (Laridae).

Sooty tern (immature), *Sterna fuscata* (Laridae).

White tern, *Gygis alba* (Laridae).

Crested tern, *Sterna bergii* (Laridae).

White-capped noddy tern, *Anous minutus* (Laridae).

Black-naped tern, *Sterna sumatrana* (Laridae).

Masked booby, *Sula dactylatra* (Sulidae).

Brown booby, *Sula leucogaster* (Sulidae).

Red-footed booby, *Sula sula* (Sulidae).

Red-footed booby chick, *Sula sula* (Sulidae).

Red-tailed tropic bird, *Phaethon rubricauda* (Phaethondidae).

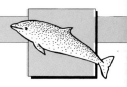

Chapter 25

Marine Mammals
Our Sea-going Relatives

Dolphins and porpoises are not truly coral reef animals, but are often encountered nearby. As we marvel at their spectacular leaps and bow-riding antics it's easy to forget these graceful fish-like creatures are actually mammals just like us. Well, not exactly! Although they possess a small amount of hair (on the tip of the snout), and suckle their young, there are few visible reminders of their mammalian links. Their sleek, muscular body is well adapted for the rigors of marine life. The upper and lower limbs are modified to form efficient fins that facilitate rapid propulsion. Dolphins can achieve speeds of up to 42 km (25 miles) per hour, exceeding that of most power boats. This ability is all the more amazing, considering the high viscosity and resultant friction of their aquatic environment.

Dolphin vs. Porpoise

What is the difference between dolphins and porpoises? None really. The two terms are used interchangeably for the same animals. Although some scientists reserve the term porpoise for small (less than 2 meters) species that lack a distinct beak and have spade-shaped (in contrast to pointed) teeth. Most of the approximately 35 species live in tropical seas, seldom venturing into cooler regions. Two of the most common types seen near coral reefs are the Spinner and Bottlenose dolphins. The latter will be familiar to anyone who has watched "Flipper" on television.

Dolphins are highly social animals. It is

very unusual to encounter a single individual. There are usually others close by. Some species travel in huge aggregations, containing several thousand individuals. More often we encounter them in groups numbering less than 100. Mothers with nursing young, immatures, and adults often form discrete groups within the schools.

How smart are they?

Dolphin intelligence has been the focus of considerable research, but there is still much to learn. Their brain is even larger and more complex than that of humans. They can be trained to perform all sorts of complex tasks. Those seen in public aquaria are just a small sample. The militia of various countries have trained dolphins to serve as "watch dogs" around secret naval installations, to retrieve important equipment from the sea floor, and even for the inhumane task of carrying lethal warheads. There remains a huge scope for their use in undersea research. One of our personal dreams is to employ them to collect fish samples and other biological specimens from deeper reefs that lie beyond the limits of SCUBA diving. With their tremendous breath-holding capacity, dolphins can stay submerged for up to 5-10 minutes and are known to dive to depths of 300 meters.

Dolphins have a relatively poor sense of taste and smell, and their vision is limited. However, they more than compensate for these short-

◀ Dugong, *Dugong dugon*.

comings with a sophisticated "sonar" system. The highly sensitive dolphin ear receives sound echoes from the surroundings and uses its sonar to echo-locate items of special interest. The brain then translates the echo patterns into a detailed "picture" of the immediate environment. The system is so accurate that a blindfolded dolphin can easily tell the difference between a live and dead fish at a considerable distance. Evidently the sonar not only perceives objects, but also relays information about their density. The sonar system makes good sense considering that sound travels five times faster in water than on land.

Baby dolphins

Growth rings on their teeth indicate that dolphins live to an age between 20 and 40 years. It takes about 5 years for a young female to reach sexual maturity. Each female is capable of producing a single offspring about every two years. Baby dolphins are comparatively large at birth, roughly one-fifth the size of an adult. They must be big enough to keep up with the school. The mother is sometimes assisted by other dolphins during birth. They help the newly emerged baby reach the surface for its critical first gulp of air. The young dolphin is constantly beside its mother and is suckled for 9 to 18 months. Considerable energy is conserved by drafting in the slipstream of the mother. During the first two years it must learn to catch food, usually consisting of fishes and squids.

Sea cows

The Sea cow or Dugong is another mammal sometimes seen near coral reefs. Although occurring over a wide area between East Africa and the Solomon Islands, they are scarce at most locations. They usually occur in shallow meadows of seagrass, which is the main item in their diet. While feeding the Dugong comes to the surface for air about once each minute. However, it is capable of staying under for up to 6-7 minutes. The usual depth range is about 1-5 meters, but a lone individual was seen in 20 meters depth off Cape York Peninsula, Australia.

The Dugong is protected in most places. The IUCN lists it as vulnerable to extinction in its Red Data Book of endangered species. Relatively large numbers are still seen in some parts of northern Australia. The largest concentration reported in recent years was off the Starcke River of eastern Cape York Peninsula. A herd containing about 600 individuals was seen from a light aircraft. Although protected in Australia, some traditional hunting by Aborigines is still allowed. Unfortunately, significant numbers are killed annually by inshore gillnets used by commercial fishermen.

Dugong live up to 75 years. Each female gives birth to a single calf about every 3-7 years. The young are suckled for about 18 months. It takes 10 years for a young female to reach maturity. Unlike dolphins, which rely on speed to catch their prey, the Dugong is a sluggish, slow-moving creature. When fully grown it reaches a length between 2-3 metres and a weight of 250-400kg.

Dugong, *Dugong dugon* (Dugongidae).

BW-15. Common dolphins of the tropical Indo-Pacific, from top to bottom: Bottlenose dolphin (*Tursiops truncatus*), Striped dolphin (*Stenella caeruleoalba*), Common dolphin (*Delphinus delphis*), Indo-Pacific humpbacked dolphin (*Sousa chinensis*), Spotted dolphin (Stenella attenuata), and Spinner dolphin *Stenella longirostris*.

Spinner dolphin, *Stenella longirostris* (Delphinidae).

Bottlenose dolphin, *Tursiops truncatus* (Delphinidae).

Index of common Names

(please note: these names refer mainly to the major groups of
organisms rather than individual species)

Genus and Species Index

Genus and Species Index

Genus and Species Index